A BOOK OF
CLASSICAL STORIES

A BOOK OF
CLASSICAL STORIES

EDITED BY

A. J. MERSON M.A.

EDITOR OF "MORE CLASSICAL STORIES"
"TALES OF WONDER" ETC.

GEORGE G. HARRAP & CO. LTD
LONDON TORONTO WELLINGTON SYDNEY

First published in Great Britain 1930
by GEORGE G. HARRAP & CO. LTD.
182 *High Holborn, London, W.C.*1

Reprinted: July 1931; *April* 1932;
July 1933; *June* 1934; *March* 1935;
September 1935; *September* 1936;
July 1937; *August* 1937;
September 1939; *June* 1941; *June* 1942;
April 1943; *February* 1944; *April* 1946;
March 1947; *August* 1948; *January* 1951;
October 1953; *November* 1954; *December* 1955

June 1956

MADE IN GREAT BRITAIN   PRINTED BY J. AND J. GRAY, EDINBURGH

NOTE

FOR permission to quote from copyright sources thanks are due to the following: Messrs G. Bell and Sons, Ltd., for quotations from Andrew Lang's *Helen of Troy* and from *Plutarch's Lives*, translated and edited by A. Stewart, M.A., and George Long, M.A.; Messrs William Blackwood and Sons, Ltd., for the quotation from Sir Theodore Martin's *Aeneid of Virgil*; Messrs Longmans, Green and Co., Ltd., and the William Morris Trustees, for the passages from *The Life and Death of Jason* and *The Doom of King Acrisius*; Messrs Macmillan and Co., Ltd., for passages from Tennyson's *Demeter and Persephone* and *The Death of Oenone*; Messrs John Murray, for passages from Professor J. W. Mackail's *The Odyssey of Homer* and Browning's *Pheidippides*; and Mrs Dora Pym, for the passages from *Readings from the Literature of Ancient Greece* and *Readings from the Literature of Ancient Rome* (Harrap).

A. J. M.

CONTENTS

7

CONTENTS

MAPS

INTRODUCTION

ONE of the most interesting boys of fiction is Tom Tulliver in *The Mill on the Floss*. When Tom returns to school after Christmas he finds that a new pupil, Philip Wakem, has arrived. Boy-like they begin to exchange experiences, and the following is part of their conversation :

" There are some lessons I'm very fond of," [said Philip]. " I'm very fond of Greek history, and everything about the Greeks. I should like to have been a Greek and fought the Persians, and then have come home and have written tragedies, or else have been listened to by everybody for my wisdom, like Socrates. . . ."

" Why, were the Greeks great fighters ? " said Tom. . . . " Is there anything like David, and Goliath, and Samson, in the Greek history ? Those are the only bits I like in the history of the Jews."

" Oh, there are very fine stories of that sort about the Greeks—about the heroes of early times who killed the wild beasts, as Samson did. And in the *Odyssey*—that's a beautiful poem—there's a more wonderful giant than Goliath—Polypheme, who had only one eye in the middle of his forehead ; and Ulysses, a little fellow, but very wise and cunning, got a red-hot pine-tree and stuck it into this one eye, and made him roar like a thousand bulls."

" Oh, what fun ! " said Tom, jumping away from the table, and stamping first with one leg and then the other. " I say, can you tell me all about those stories ? Because I shan't learn Greek, you know. . . . Shall I ? " he added, pausing in his stamping with a sudden alarm, lest the contrary might be possible. " Does every gentleman

learn Greek ? . . . . Will Mr Stelling make me begin with
it, do you think ? "

"No, I should think not—very likely not," said Philip.
"But you may read those stories without knowing Greek.
I've got them in English."

One of the objects of this book is to tell you something
of the stories and heroes of whom Philip speaks. For
one of our legacies from Greece and Rome is a wealth
of stories which have become world-famous, and which
have not only inspired our writers and artists, but have
also, as it were, become part of our common speech.
We speak of a person being as strong as Hercules or being
set to a Herculean task ; a very wealthy person is as rich
as Croesus ; a spare diet is Spartan fare ; while such
words as tantalize, stentorian, vulcanite, and atlas are
from classical proper names.

Many of these stories have often been told in English,
and, in addition, our poetry is full of allusions to them.
Although Shakespeare, it is said, knew little Latin and
less Greek, he knew classical mythology and history and
drew on these for many of his similes and comparisons,
as well as for some of his plays. When he makes Bassanio
in *The Merchant of Venice* describe Portia of Belmont he
says :

> And her sunny locks
> Hang on her temples like a golden fleece ;
> Which makes her seat of Belmont Colchos' strand,
> And many Jasons come in quest of her.

In *The Winter's Tale* Perdita, in giving flowers to her
guests, says :

> Now, my fair'st friend,
> I would I had some flowers o' the spring that might
> Become your time of day. . . .
>
> O, Proserpina,
> For the flowers now, that frighted thou let'st fall

From Dis's waggon ! daffodils,
That come before the swallow dares, and take
The winds of March with beauty : violets dim,
But sweeter than the lids of Juno's eyes
Or Cytherea's breath ; pale primroses,
That die unmarried, ere they can behold
Bright Phoebus in his strength.

Milton makes even more use of these stories, as we should expect, since he was the foremost classical scholar of his day. In one of his poems he wishes to hear such sweet music

> That Orpheus' self may heave his head
> From golden slumber, on a bed
> Of heaped Elysian flowers, and hear
> Such strains as would have won the ear
> Of Pluto, to have quite set free
> His half-regained Eurydice.

In one poem Shelley mentions the *Argo*, Orpheus, Ulysses, and the tale of Troy ; Byron's poem, *The Isles of Greece*, is full of references to the great deeds of the ancient Greeks ; the Private of the Buffs, of whom Sir F. H. Doyle sings,

> died, as firm as Sparta's King,
> Because his soul was great ;

while in *A Christmas Hymn* (Domett), we are told that

> Peace brooded o'er the hushed domain,
> Apollo, Pallas, Jove, and Mars,
> Held undisturbed their ancient reign,
> In the solemn midnight,
> Centuries ago !

The stories in this book will help you to understand these allusions and to appreciate the poems in which they occur. But it is hoped you will read the stories for their own sakes, for there are no better stories in literature.

Tom Tulliver's feelings were stirred, as you have read,

when he first heard of those stories. Fighting and adventure were " great fun " to him, and here there are both in plenty.   Among those ancient peoples " a man was honoured, not because he happened to be rich, but according to his skill, and his strength, and his courage, and the number of things he could do." Difficulty and danger but drove them on to greater deeds, for they considered it " better to die in the flower of youth, on the chance of winning a noble name, than to live at ease like the sheep, and die unloved and unrenowned." Philip Wakem, too, deformed as he was, delighted in the stories, but while he recognized their power, he also felt their charm. His discovery of them must have been an experience as thrilling as that described by John Keats in his sonnet *On First Looking into Chapman's Homer*. Keats could not read Greek, and he first read the wonderful story of Troy in a translation made by the Elizabethan poet George Chapman.

> Much have I travell'd in the realms of gold,
>   And many goodly states and kingdoms seen ;
>   Round many western islands have I been
> Which bards in fealty to Apollo hold.
> Oft of one wide expanse had I been told
>   That deep-brow'd Homer ruled as his demesne ;
>   Yet did I never breathe its pure serene
> Till I heard Chapman speak out loud and bold :
> Then felt I like some watcher of the skies
>   When a new planet swims into his ken ;
> Or like stout Cortez when with eagle eyes
>   He star'd at the Pacific—and all his men
> Look'd at each other with a wild surmise—
>   Silent, upon a peak in Darien.

Naturally, only a few of the numerous classical stories which have come down to us, and in cases only parts of these, could be included in this collection.   You will, no doubt, wish to read more of them, and to enable you to find them there has been added a suggested list for further reading.

It should be explained that, here and there, editorial liberties have been taken with the passages selected. Excisions have been made or brief explanations inserted for the sake of brevity and clarity, and it has not been thought necessary or expedient to indicate these in all cases.

GREECE
AND
AEGAEAN SEA

R. Strymon
MACEDONIA
Amphi
Aegae
Pella
Therma
(Thessalonica)
Chalcidi
Methone
Olynthus
Pydna
EPIRUS
Mt Olympus
Potidaea
Mende
Scione
Mt Ossa
Corcyra
•Dodona
Peneus R.
•Larissa
THESSALIA
Mt Pelion
Crannon
Pagasae
•Pherae
Pagasaean Gulf
Pharsalus•
Arcamisium
Histiaea
Leucas
Malian G.
Thermopylae
LOCRIS
EU
ACARNANIA
AETOLIA
PHOCIS
R. Achelous
Mt Parnassus
Delphi
Ithaca
Naupactus
Chaeronea
LOCRIS
Cirrha
Mt Helicon
BOEOTIA
Cephallenia
Rhium
Corinthian Gulf
Aegae
Thebes
Leuctra•
Plataea
Eleusis
Dyme
ACHAIA
Sicyon
Megara
Saronic
Cyllene
peneus
Corinth
R.
Zacynthos
Elis
Orchomenus• Mycenae
ARGOLIS
Olympia
Pisa
Argos
Epidaurus
Gu
R. Alpheus
ARCADIA
Tiryns
Troezen
Triphylia
Mantineia
•Tegea
Argolic Gulf
Megalopolis
Mt Ithome
Mt Parnon
MESSENIA
Messene
LACONICA
Sparta•
•Amyclae
Pylos
Sphacteria
IONIAN SEA

CRETE
on same scale

Cape Psacon
Cape Taenarum
Cape Malea
Lissus
Cnossus•
Olus•
Ida Mt
Dicte Mt
Cythera
•Gortyna
Phaestus

Abdera

Thasos

Samothrace

Athos

Lemnos

Imbros

Horiscus · Hebr

Perinthus

Byzantium

P R O P O N T I S

Cyzicus

Hellespont

Aegospotami

Lampsacus

Abydos

Simois R.

Troja

Old Scamander

Scamander R.

Antandros

Tenedos

Mt. Ida

PHRYGIA

HELLESPONTICA

Adramyttium

Methymna

MYSIA

Mytilene

Pergamum

Lesbos

Pitane

LYDIA

Cyme

Phocaea

R. Hermus

Magnesia

Old Smyrna

Sardis

New Smyrna

Mt. Tmolus

Chios

Erythrae

Clazomenae

Scyros

Lebedos

R. Cayster

Colophon

Andros

Ephesus

Magnesia

R. Maeander

Tenos

Icaria

Samos

Priene

CARIA

Myus

Miletus

Delos

Paros

Naxos

Halicarnassus

Ios

Amorgos

Cnidus

Thera

Ialysus

Rhodes

Camirus

CRETE

A E G A E A N   S E A

AEOLIS

IONIA

CHERSONESUS

English Miles

0   10   20   30   40   50   60

Jⁿ Mᶜ Donald, Edinburgh.

LEGENDS AND MYTHS

ORPHEUS

ORPHEUS with his lute made trees,
And the mountain tops that freeze,
   Bow themselves when he did sing ;
To his music plants and flowers
Ever sprung, as sun and showers
   There had made a lasting spring.

Everything that heard him play,
Even the billows of the sea,
   Hung their heads, and then lay by.
In sweet music is such art,
Killing care and grief of heart
   Fall asleep, or hearing, die.

WILLIAM SHAKESPEARE

ORPHEUS AND EURYDICE

IN a pleasant valley in Thrace, among springing flowers and
the happy songs of the birds, dwelt Orpheus, the first and
greatest of musicians. By his wonderful playing he so
charmed the hearts of men that they forgot their angry
passions and evil desires and became gentle like little
children. Even rocks and trees would leave their resting-
places and come near to listen, while wild beasts became
tame and harmless under the spell of his music.

Orpheus had a beautiful wife, Eurydice, and her
sisters, the nymphs of the valley, living near by, bore them
company. Their life was a bright and wonderful thing,

with the music of Orpheus running through it like a magical thread, till a sudden and terrible mischance befell. Eurydice, treading unwittingly on a serpent, was bitten in the foot, and, in spite of all that Orpheus and the nymphs could do, after a few hours of suffering she died, and her spirit fled to the Underworld, where Pluto the king and Persephone his young queen ruled over those who had died and been carried to Hades.

Now indeed were the days darkened for Orpheus. Nothing, not even his beloved lyre, could drag him from the depths of sorrow into which he had fallen, and at length, despairing of ever finding happiness without Eurydice, he determined to journey to Hades and implore Pluto to restore his lost bride to him. Many were the difficulties of that dread journey. The ferryman, Charon, refused to allow him to cross the river Styx ; he had to face the fierce three-headed dog, the terrible Cerberus, which guarded the entrance to Pluto's realm ; but his music so charmed these that he was allowed to pass.

Still playing on his lute, he sped down the dark passages of Hades, and the spirits undergoing punishment blessed his coming, for Ixion's wheel was stayed for a space, and for a space Tantalus forgot his raging hunger and thirst. At last he entered Pluto's presence, and before the King could protest at a living mortal thus appearing before him, Orpheus had poured forth the story of his grief and longing in a song surpassingly sweet and poignant, which so wrought upon even Pluto's hard heart that he consented to give up Eurydice and allow her to return to earth. One condition he made. Till he had reached the upper air and was quite free of the kingdom of Hades, he was to trust the King's word that Eurydice was following him and cast not so much as a glance behind.

Joyfully Orpheus set out on the return journey. The shadows of the Underworld were yielding to the pleasant light of day, when, moved by some inexplicable terror, Orpheus glanced back to see if Eurydice were really following. Too late he remembered the penalty of his want of faith. He saw the form of his beloved fade away into the gloom of Hades, her arms stretched out toward him longingly but helplessly, and although he lingered for days hoping for another chance, he had at length to return alone—but not to the happy valley. That, without his bride, he could not bear, and he retired to the hills alone, where, for a few months, the sad wailing of his lute could be heard. Then that ceased, and no one knew what became of Orpheus. Some say he was killed by a band of Thracian dancing-women because he would not play merry music to them—he whose heart had no joy left in it—but at the last he and his Eurydice were united for ever in the Kingdom of the Dead.

J. M. M.

THE ARGONAUTS

THE GOLDEN FLEECE

THE old Hellens said that the Golden Fleece hung in Colchis, which we call the Circassian coast, nailed to a beech-tree in the War-god's wood ; and that it was the fleece of the wondrous ram who bore Phrixus and Helle across the Euxine sea. For Phrixus and Helle were the children of the cloud-nymph, and of Athamas the Minuan king. And when a famine came upon the land, their cruel step-mother Ino wished to kill them, that her own children might reign, and said that they must be sacrificed on an altar, to turn away the anger of the Gods. So the poor children were brought to the altar, and the priest stood ready with his knife, when out of the clouds came the Golden Ram, and took them on his back, and vanished.

He carried the children far away over land and sea, till he came to the Thracian Chersonese, and Helle fell into the sea. So those narrow straits are called " Hellespont," after her ; and they bear that name until this day.

Then the ram flew on with Phrixus to the north-east across the sea which we call the Black Sea now ; but the Hellens call it Euxine. And at last, they say, he stopped at Colchis, on the steep Circassian coast ; and there Phrixus married Chalciope, the daughter of Aietes the king ; and offered the ram in sacrifice ; and Aietes nailed the ram's fleece to a beech, in the grove of Ares the War-god.

And after a while Phrixus died, and was buried, but his spirit had no rest ; for he was buried far from his native land, and the pleasant hills of Hellas. So he came in dreams to the heroes of the Minuai, and called sadly by their beds, " Come and set my spirit free, that I may go home to my fathers and to my kinfolk, and the pleasant Minuan land."

And they asked, " How shall we set your spirit free ? "

" You must sail over the sea to Colchis, and bring home the Golden Fleece ; and then my spirit will come back with it, and I shall sleep with my fathers and have rest."

He came thus, and called to them often ; but when they woke they looked at each other, and said, " Who dare sail to Colchis, or bring home the Golden Fleece ? " And in all the country none was brave enough to try it ; for the man and the time were not come.

At last Jason was tricked by his uncle, Pelias, who was jealous of him and thought to get rid of him thus, into promising to undertake the quest of the Fleece.

So the heralds went out, and cried to all the heroes of the Minuai, " Who dare come to the adventure of the Golden Fleece ? "

And Hera stirred the hearts of all the princes, and they

came from all their valleys to the yellow sands of Pagasai. And first came Heracles the mighty, with his lion's skin and club, and behind him Hylas, his young squire, who bore his arrows and his bow; and Tiphys, the skilful steersman; and Butes, the fairest of all men; and Castor and Polydeuces the twins, the sons of the magic swan; and Caineus, the strongest of mortals, whom the Centaurs tried in vain to kill, and overwhelmed him with trunks of pine-trees, but even so he would not die; and thither came Zetes and Calais, the winged sons of the North Wind; and Peleus, the father of Achilles, whose bride was silver-footed Thetis, the goddess of the sea. And thither came Telamon and Oileus, the fathers of the two Aiantes, who fought upon the plains of Troy; and Mopsus, the wise soothsayer, who knew the speech of birds; and Idmon, to whom Phoebus gave a tongue to prophesy of things to come; and Ancaios, who could read the stars, and knew all the circles of the heavens; and Argus, the famed shipbuilder, and many a hero more, in helmets of brass and gold, with tall dyed horse-hair crests, and embroidered shirts of linen beneath their coats of mail, and greaves of polished tin to guard their knees in fight; with each man his shield upon his shoulder, of many a fold of tough bull's hide, and his sword of tempered bronze in his silver-studded belt; and in his right hand a pair of lances, of the heavy white ash-staves.

So they came down to Iolcos, and all the city came out to meet them, and were never tired with looking at their height, and their beauty, and their gallant bearing, and the glitter of their inlaid arms. And some said, " Never was such a gathering of the heroes since the Hellens conquered the land." But the women sighed over them, and whispered, "Alas! they are all going to their death!"

CHARLES KINGSLEY, *The Heroes* (adapted)

THE BUILDING OF "ARGO"

THEN they felled the pines on Pelion, and shaped them with the axe, and Argus taught them to build a galley, the first long ship which ever sailed the seas. They pierced her for fifty oars—an oar for each hero of the crew—and pitched her with coal-black pitch, and painted her bows with vermilion ; and they named her *Argo*, after Argus, and worked at her all day long. And at night Pelias feasted them like a king, and they slept in his palace porch.

But Jason went away to the northward, and into the land of Thrace, till he found Orpheus, the prince of minstrels, where he dwelt in his cave under Rhodope, among the savage Cicon tribes. And he asked him, " Will you leave your mountains, Orpheus, my fellow-scholar in old times, and cross Strymon once more with me, to sail with the heroes of the Minuai, and bring home the Golden Fleece, and charm for us all men and all monsters with your magic harp and song ? "

Then Orpheus sighed, " Have I not had enough of toil and of weary wandering far and wide since I lived in Cheiron's cave, above Iolcos by the sea ? In vain is the skill and the voice which my goddess mother gave me ; in vain have I sung and laboured ; in vain I went down to the dead, and charmed all the kings of Hades, to win back Eurydice my bride. For I won her, my beloved, and lost her again the same day, and wandered away in my madness, even to Egypt and the Libyan sands, and the isles of all the seas, driven on by the terrible gadfly, while I charmed in vain the hearts of men, and the savage forest beasts, and the trees and the lifeless stones, with my magic harp and song, giving rest, but finding none. But at last Calliope, my mother, delivered me, and brought me home in peace ; and I dwell here in the cave alone, among the savage Cicon tribes, softening their wild hearts with music and the gentle laws of Zeus. And now I must go out again, to the ends of all the earth, far away into the misty darkness, to the last wave of the Eastern Sea. But what is doomed must be, and a friend's demand obeyed ; for prayers are the daughters of Zeus, and who honours them honours him."

Then Orpheus rose up sighing, and took his harp, and went over Strymon. And he led Jason to the south-west, up the banks of Haliacmon and over the spurs of Pindus, to Dodona, the town of Zeus, where it stood by the side of the sacred lake, and the fountain which breathed out fire, in the darkness of the ancient oakwood, beneath the mountain of the hundred springs. And he led him to the holy oak, where the black dove settled in old times, and was changed into the priestess of Zeus, and gave oracles to all nations round. And he bade him cut down a bough, and sacrifice to Hera and to Zeus ; and they took the bough and came to Iolcos, and nailed it to the beak-head of the ship.

And at last the ship was finished, and they tried to launch her down the beach ; but she was too heavy for them to move her, and her keel sank deep into the sand. Then all the heroes looked at each other blushing ; but Jason spoke, and said, " Let us ask the magic bough ; perhaps it can help us in our need."

Then a voice came from the bough, and Jason heard the words it said, and bade Orpheus play upon the harp, while the heroes waited round, holding the pine-trunk rollers, to help her toward the sea.

Then Orpheus took his harp, and began his magic song : " How sweet it is to ride upon the surges, and to leap from wave to wave, while the wind sings cheerful in the cordage, and the oars flash fast among the foam ! How sweet it is to roam across the ocean, and see new towns and wondrous lands, and to come home laden with treasure, and to win undying fame ! "

And the good ship *Argo* heard him, and longed to be away and out at sea ; till she stirred in every timber, and heaved from stem to stern, and leapt up from the sand upon the rollers, and plunged onward like a gallant horse ; and the heroes fed her path with pine-trunks, till she rushed into the whispering sea.

Then they stored her well with food and water, and pulled the ladder up on board, and settled themselves each man to his oar, and kept time to Orpheus' harp ; and away across the bay they rowed southward, while the people lined the cliffs ; and the women wept, while the men shouted, at the starting of that gallant crew.

CHARLES KINGSLEY, *The Heroes*

THE OUTWARD JOURNEY

THERE was no lack of wonderful events. At a certain island they were hospitably received by King Cyzicus, its sovereign, who made a feast for them, and treated them like brothers. But the Argonauts saw that this good king looked downcast and very much troubled, and they inquired of him what was the matter. King Cyzicus informed them that he and his subjects were greatly abused and incommoded by the inhabitants of a neighbouring mountain, who made war upon them, and killed many people, and ravaged the country. And while they were talking about it, Cyzicus pointed to the mountain, and asked Jason and his companions what they saw there.

" I see some very tall objects," answered Jason ; " but they are at such a distance that I cannot distinctly make out what they are. To tell your Majesty the truth, they look so very strangely that I am inclined to think them clouds, which have chanced to take something like human shapes."

" I see them very plainly," remarked Lynceus, whose eyes, you know, were as far-sighted as a telescope. " They are a band of enormous giants, all of whom have six arms apiece, and a club, a sword, or some other weapon in each of their hands."

" You have excellent eyes," said King Cyzicus. " Yes ; they are six-armed giants, as you say, and these are the enemies whom I and my subjects have to contend with."

The next day, when the Argonauts were about setting sail, down came these terrible giants, stepping a hundred yards at a stride, brandishing their six arms apiece, and looking very formidable, so far aloft in the air. Each of these monsters was able to carry on a whole war by himself ; for with one of his arms he could fling immense stones, and wield a club with another, and a sword with a third, while a fourth was poking a long spear at the enemy, and the fifth and sixth were shooting him with a bow and arrow. But, luckily, though the giants were so huge, and had so many arms, they had each but one heart, and that no bigger nor braver than the heart of an ordinary man. Besides, if they had been like the hundred-armed Briareus, the brave Argonauts would have given them their hands full of fight. Jason and his friends went boldly to meet them, slew a great many, and made the rest take to their heels, so that, if the giants had had six legs apiece instead of six arms, it would have served them better to run away with.

Another strange adventure happened when the voyagers came to Thrace, where they found a poor blind king, named Phineus, deserted by his subjects, and living in a very sorrowful way, all by himself.

On Jason's inquiring whether they could do him any service, the king answered that he was terribly tormented by three great winged creatures, called Harpies, which had the faces of women, and the wings, bodies, and claws of vultures. These ugly wretches were in the habit of snatching away his dinner, and allowed him no peace of his life. Upon hearing this, the Argonauts spread a plentiful feast on the sea-shore, well knowing, from what the blind king said of their greediness, that the Harpies would snuff up the scent of the victuals, and quickly come to steal them away. And so it turned out ; for, hardly was the table set, before the three hideous vulture-women came flapping their wings, seized the food in their talons, and flew off as fast as they could. But the two sons of the North Wind drew their swords, spread their pinions, and set off through the air in pursuit of the thieves, whom they at last overtook among some islands, after a chase of hundreds of miles. The two winged youths blustered terribly at the Harpies (for they had the rough temper of their father), and so frightened them with their drawn swords, that they solemnly promised never to trouble King Phineus again.

NATHANIEL HAWTHORNE, *Tanglewood Tales*

THE WINNING OF THE FLEECE

AT last the heroes saw the dark stream of Phasis rushing headlong to the sea, and, shining above the tree-tops, the golden roofs of King Aietes, the child of the Sun. And Aietes came down in his golden chariot, and his daughters by his side, Medeia the fair witch-maiden, and Chalciope, who had been Phrixus' wife, and behind him a crowd of servants and soldiers, for he was a rich and mighty prince.

And as he drove down by the reedy river he saw *Argo* sliding up beneath the bank, and many a hero in her, like Immortals for beauty and for strength, as their weapons glittered round them in the level morning sunlight, through the white mist of the stream. But Jason was the noblest of all ; for Hera, who loved him, gave him beauty and tallness and terrible manhood.

And when they came near together and looked into each other's eyes the heroes were awed before Aietes as he shone in his chariot, like his father the glorious Sun ; for his robes were of rich gold tissue, and the rays of his diadem flashed fire ; and in his hand he bore a jewelled sceptre, which glittered like the stars ; and sternly he looked at them under his brows, and sternly he spoke and loud :

" Who are you, and what want you here, that you come to the shore of Cutaia ? Do you take no account of my rule, nor of my people the Colchians who serve me, who never tired yet in the battle, and know well how to face an invader ? "

And the heroes sat silent awhile before the face of that ancient king. But Hera the awful goddess put courage into Jason's heart, and he rose and shouted loudly in answer, " We are no pirates nor lawless men. We come not to plunder and to ravage, or carry away slaves from your land ; but my uncle, the son of Poseidon, Pelias the Minuan king, he it is who has set me on a quest to bring home the Golden Fleece. And these too, my bold comrades, they are no nameless men ; for some are the sons of Immortals, and some of heroes far renowned. And we too never tire in battle, and know well how to give blows and to take ; yet we wish to be guests at your table ; it will be better so for both."

Then Aietes' rage rushed up like a whirlwind, and his eyes flashed fire as he heard ; but he crushed his anger down in his breast, and spoke mildly a cunning speech :

" If you will fight for the Fleece with my Colchians, then many a man must die. But do you indeed expect to win from me the Fleece in fight ? So few you are that if you be worsted I can load your ship with your corpses.

But if you will be ruled by me, you will find it better far to choose the best man among you, and let him fulfil the labours which I demand. Then I will give him the Golden Fleece for a prize and a glory to you all."

So saying, he turned his horses and drove back in silence to the town. And the Minuai sat silent with sorrow, and longed for Heracles and his strength; for there was no facing the thousands of the Colchians and the fearful chance of war.

But Chalciope, Phrixus' widow, went weeping to the town; for she remembered her Minuan husband, and all the pleasures of her youth, while she watched the fair faces of his kinsmen, and their long locks of golden hair. And she whispered to Medeia her sister, " Why should all these brave men die? Why does not my father give them up the Fleece, that my husband's spirit may have rest?"

And Medeia's heart pitied the heroes, and Jason most of all; and she answered, " Our father is stern and terrible, and who can win the Golden Fleece?" But Chalciope said, " These men are not like our men; there is nothing which they cannot dare nor do."

And Medeia thought of Jason and his brave countenance and said, " If there was one among them who knew no fear, I could show him how to win the Fleece."

[In the night-time Medeia came down secretly to *Argo*, and told Jason what he must do. He must tame the two brazen-footed bulls who breathed devouring flame; and with them he must plough ere nightfall four acres in the field of Ares; and he must sow them with serpents' teeth, of which each tooth would spring up into an armed man. Then he must fight with all those warriors; and then he must pass the serpent which guarded the Fleece. She showed him how he might overcome all these difficulties, and gave him a vase of magic ointment.]

At sunrise Jason went and bathed, and anointed himself from head to foot, and his shield, and his helmet, and his weapons, and bade his comrades try the spell. So they tried to bend his lance, but it stood like an iron bar; and Idas in spite hewed at it with his sword, but the blade flew to splinters in his face. Then they hurled their lances at his shield, but the spear-points turned like lead; and Caineus tried to throw him, but he never stirred a foot; and Polydeuces struck him with his fist a blow which would have killed an ox, but Jason only smiled, and the heroes danced about him with delight; and he leapt, and ran, and shouted in the joy of that enormous strength, till the sun rose, and it was time to go and to claim Aietes' promise.

So he sent up Telamon and Aithalides to tell Aietes that he was ready for the fight; and they went up among the marble walls, and beneath the roofs of gold, and stood in Aietes' hall, while he grew pale with rage.

" Fulfil your promise to us, child of the blazing Sun. Give us the serpents' teeth, and let loose the fiery bulls; for we have found a champion among us who can win the Golden Fleece."

And Aietes bit his lips, for he fancied that they had fled away by night: but he could not go back from his promise; so he gave them the serpents' teeth.

Then he called for his chariot and his horses, and sent heralds through all the town; and all the people went out with him to the dreadful War-god's field.

And there Aietes sat upon his throne, with his warriors on each hand, thousands and tens of thousands, clothed from head to foot in steel chain-mail. And the people and the women crowded to every window and bank and wall; while the Minuai stood together, a mere handful in the midst of that great host.

And Chalciope was there, and Medeia, wrapped closely

in her veil ; but Aietes did not know that she was muttering cunning spells between her lips.

Then Jason cried, " Fulfil your promise, and let your fiery bulls come forth."

Then Aietes bade open the gates, and the magic bulls leapt out. Their brazen hoofs rang upon the ground, and their nostrils sent out sheets of flame, as they rushed with lowered heads upon Jason ; but he never flinched a step. The flame of their breath swept round him, but it singed not a hair of his head ; and the bulls stopped short and trembled when Medeia began her spell.

Then Jason sprang upon the nearest and seized him by the horn ; and up and down they wrestled, till the bull fell grovelling on his knees ; for the heart of the brute died within him, and his mighty limbs were loosed, beneath the steadfast eye of that dark witch-maiden and the magic whisper of her lips.

So both the bulls were tamed and yoked ; and Jason bound them to the plough, and goaded them onward with his lance till he had ploughed the sacred field.

And all the Minuai shouted ; but Aietes bit his lips with rage, for the half of Jason's work was over, and the sun was yet high in heaven.

Then he took the serpents' teeth and sowed them, and waited what would befall. But Medeia looked at him and at his helmet, lest he should forget the lesson she had taught.

And every furrow heaved and bubbled, and out of every clod arose a man. Out of the earth they rose by thousands, each clad from head to foot in steel, and drew their swords and rushed on Jason, where he stood in the midst alone.

Then the Minuai grew pale with fear for him ; but Aietes laughed a bitter laugh. " See ! if I had not warriors enough already round me, I could call them out of the bosom of the earth."

But Jason snatched off his helmet, and hurled it into the thickest of the throng. And blind madness came upon them, suspicion, hate, and fear; and one cried to his fellow, "Thou didst strike me!" and another, "Thou art Jason; thou shalt die!" So fury seized those earth-born phantoms, and each turned his hand against the rest; and they fought and were never weary, till they all lay dead upon the ground. Then the magic furrows opened, and the kind earth took them home into her breast; and the grass grew up all green again above them, and Jason's work was done.

Then the Minuai rose and shouted, till Prometheus heard them from his crag. And Jason cried, "Lead me to the Fleece this moment, before the sun goes down."

But Aietes thought, "He has conquered the bulls, and sown and reaped the deadly crop. Who is this who is proof against all magic? He may kill the serpent yet." So he delayed, and sat taking counsel with his princes till the sun went down and all was dark. Then he bade a herald cry, "Every man to his home for to-night. To-morrow we will meet these heroes, and speak about the Golden Fleece."

[Again Medeia came to the Argonauts and agreed to help them on condition that they would take her with them back to Iolcos.]

So at midnight Jason and Orpheus went up the bank, and found Medeia; and beside came Absyrtus her young brother, leading a yearling lamb.

Then Medeia brought them to a thicket beside the War-god's gate; and there she bade Jason dig a ditch, and kill the lamb, and leave it there, and strew on it magic herbs and honey from the honeycomb.

Then sprang up through the earth, with the red fire flashing before her, Brimo the wild witch-huntress, while her mad hounds howled around. She had one head like a horse's, and another like a ravening hound's, and another like a hissing snake's, and a sword in either hand. And she leapt into the ditch with her hounds, and they ate and drank their fill, while Jason and Orpheus trembled, and Medeia hid her eyes. And at last the witch-queen vanished, and fled with her hounds into the woods; and the bars of the gates fell down, and the brazen doors flew wide, and Medeia and the heroes ran forward and hurried through the poison wood, among the dark stems of the mighty beeches, guided by the gleam of the Golden Fleece, until they saw it hanging on one vast tree in the midst. And Jason would have sprung to seize it; but Medeia held him back, and pointed, shuddering, to the tree-foot, where the mighty serpent lay, coiled in and out among the roots, with a body like a mountain pine. His coils stretched many a fathom, spangled with bronze and gold; and half of him they could see, but no more, for the rest lay in the darkness far beyond.

And when he saw them coming he lifted up his head, and watched them with his small bright eyes, and flashed his forked tongue, and roared like the fire among the woodlands, till the forest tossed and groaned. For his cries shook the trees from leaf to root, and swept over the long reaches of the river, and over Aietes' hall, and woke the sleepers in the city, till mothers clasped their children in their fear.

But Medeia called gently to him; and he stretched out his long spotted neck, and licked her hand, and looked up in her face, as if to ask for food. Then she made a sign to Orpheus, and he began his magic song.

And as he sang, the forest grew calm again, and the leaves on every tree hung still; and the serpent's head sank down, and his brazen coils grew limp, and his glittering eyes closed lazily, till he breathed as gently

as a child, while Orpheus called to pleasant Slumber,
who gives peace to men, and beasts, and waves.

Then Jason leapt forward warily, and stepped across
that mighty snake, and tore the Fleece from off the tree-
trunk.

> Then swiftly did they leave the dreadful place,
> Turning no look behind, and reached the street,
> That with familiar look and kind did greet
> Those wanderers, mazed with marvels and with fear.
> And so, unchallenged, did they draw anear
> The long white quays, and at the street's end now
> Beheld the ships' masts standing row by row
> Stark black against the stars : then cautiously
> Peered Jason forth, ere they took heart to try
> The open starlit place ; but nought he saw
> Except the night-wind twitching the loose straw
> From half-unloaded keels, and nought he heard
> But the strange twittering of a caged green bird
> Within an Indian ship, and from the hill
> A distant baying : yea, all was so still,
> Somewhat they doubted, natheless forth they passed,
> And *Argo's* painted sides they reached at last.
> On whom down-looking, scarce more noise they heard
> Than from the other ships ; some muttered word,
> Some creaking of the timbers, as the tide
> Ran gurgling seaward past her shielded side.
> Then Jason knelt, and whispered : " Wise ye be,
> O fair companions on the pathless sea,
> But come, Erginus, Nestor, and ye twain
> Of Lacedaemon, to behold my gain ;
> Take me amongst you, neither be afraid
> To take withal this gold, and this fair maid.
> Yare !—for the ebb runs strongly towards the sea,
> The east wind drives the rack to Thessaly,

c

And lightly do such kings as this one sleep
If now and then small watch their servants keep."
Then saw Medeia men like shadows grey,
Rise from the darksome decks, who took straightway
With murmured joy, from Jason's outstretched hands,
The conquered Fleece, the wonder of all lands,
While with strong arms he took the royal maid,
And in their hold the precious burthen laid,
And scarce her dainty feet could touch the deck,
Ere down he leapt, and little now did reck
That loudly clanged his armour therewithal.[1]

Then Jason cried, " Go now, good *Argo*, swift and steady, if ever you would see Pelion more." And she went, as the heroes drove her, grim and silent all, with muffled oars, till the pine-wood bent like willow in their hands, and stout *Argo* groaned beneath their strokes.

On and on, beneath the dewy darkness, they fled swiftly down the swirling stream ; underneath black walls, and temples, and the castles of the princes of the East ; past sluice-mouths, and fragrant gardens, and groves of all strange fruits ; past marshes where fat kine lay sleeping, and long beds of whispering reeds ; till they heard the merry music of the surge upon the bar, as it tumbled in the moonlight all alone.

Into the surge they rushed, and *Argo* leapt the breakers like a horse ; for she knew the time was come to show her mettle, and win honour for the heroes and herself.

Into the surge they rushed, and *Argo* leapt the breakers like a horse, till the heroes stopped all panting, each man upon his oar, as she slid into the still, broad sea.

[1] From *The Life and Death of Jason*, by William Morris. The interpolation of these lines, and those on p. 35, in Kingsley's text is, of course, the present editor's.

Then Orpheus took his harp and sang a paean, till the heroes' hearts rose high again; and they rowed on stoutly and steadfastly, away into the darkness of the West.

> So sung he joyously, nor knew that they
> Must wander yet for many an evil day
> Or ever the dread Gods should let them come
> Back to the white walls of their long-left home.

CHARLES KINGSLEY, The Heroes

THE RETURN JOURNEY

[VARIOUS accounts are given of the voyage home, but all agree that after many dangers they came to Circe's isle, and then sailed eastward], by Tartessus on the Iberian shore, till they came to the Pillars of Hercules, and the Mediterranean Sea. And thence they sailed on through the deeps of Sardinia, and past the Ausonian islands, and the capes of the Tyrrhenian shore, till they came to a flowery island, upon a still bright summer's eve. And as they neared it, slowly and wearily, they heard sweet songs upon the shore. But when Medeia heard it, she started, and cried, "Beware, all heroes, for these are the rocks of the Sirens. You must pass close by them, for there is no other channel; but those who listen to that song are lost."

Then Orpheus spoke, the king of all minstrels, "Let them match their song against mine. I have charmed stones, and trees, and dragons, how much more the hearts of men!" So he caught up his lyre, and stood upon the poop, and began his magic song.

And now they could see the Sirens on Anthemousa, the flowery isle; three fair maidens sitting on the beach, beneath a red rock in the setting sun, among beds of crimson poppies and golden asphodel. Slowly they sung and sleepily, with silver voices, mild and clear, which stole over the golden waters and into the hearts of all the heroes, in spite of Orpheus' song.

And all things stayed around and listened ; the gulls sat in white lines along the rocks ; on the beach great seals lay basking, and kept time with lazy heads ; while silver shoals of fish came up to hearken, and whispered as they broke the shining calm. The Wind overhead hushed his whistling, as he shepherded his clouds toward the west ; and the clouds stood in mid blue, and listened dreaming, like a flock of golden sheep.

And as the heroes listened, the oars fell from their hands, and their heads drooped on their breasts, and they closed their heavy eyes ; and they dreamed of bright, still gardens, and of slumbers under murmuring pines, till all their toil seemed foolishness, and they thought of their renown no more.

Then one lifted his head suddenly, and cried, " What use in wandering for ever ? Let us stay here and rest awhile." And another, " Let us row to the shore, and hear the words they sing." And another, " I care not for the words, but for the music. They shall sing me to sleep, that I may rest."

And Butes, the son of Pandion, the fairest of all mortal men, leapt out and swam toward the shore, crying, " I come, I come, fair maidens, to live and die here, listening to your song."

Then Medeia clapped her hands together, and cried, " Sing louder, Orpheus, sing a bolder strain ; wake up these hapless sluggards, or none of them will see the land of Hellas more."

Then Orpheus lifted his harp, and crashed his cunning hand across the strings ; and his music and his voice rose like a trumpet through the still evening air ; into the air it rushed like thunder, till the rocks rang and the sea; and into their souls it rushed like wine, till all hearts beat fast within their breasts.

And he sung the song of Perseus, how the Gods led him over land and sea, and how he slew the loathly Gorgon, and won himself a peerless bride; and how he sits now with the Gods upon Olympus, a shining star in the sky, immortal with his immortal bride, and honoured by all men below.

So Orpheus sang, and the Sirens, answering each other across the golden sea, till Orpheus' voice drowned the Sirens', and the heroes caught their oars again.

And they cried, "We will be men like Perseus, and we will dare and suffer to the last. Sing us his song again, brave Orpheus, that we may forget the Sirens and their spell."

And as Orpheus sang, they dashed their oars into the sea, and kept time to his music, as they fled fast away; and the Sirens' voices died behind them, in the hissing of the foam along their wake.

But Butes swam to the shore, and knelt down before the Sirens, and cried, "Sing on! Sing on!" But he could say no more, for a charmed sleep came over him, and a pleasant humming in his ears; and he sank all along upon the pebbles, and forgot all heaven and earth, and never looked at that sad beach around him, all strewn with the bones of men.

Then slowly rose up those three fair sisters, with a cruel smile upon their lips; and slowly they crept down towards him, like leopards who creep upon their prey; and their hands were like the talons of eagles as they stept across the bones of their victims to enjoy their cruel feast.

But fairest Aphrodite saw him from the highest Idalian peak, and she pitied his youth and his beauty, and leapt up from her golden throne; and like a falling star she cleft the sky, and left a trail of glittering light, till she stooped to the Isle of the Sirens, and snatched their prey from their claws. And she lifted Butes as he lay sleeping, and wrapt him in a golden mist ; and she bore him to the peak of Lilybaeum, and he slept there many a pleasant year.

But when the Sirens saw that they were conquered, they shrieked for envy and rage, and leapt from the beach into the sea, and were changed into rocks until this day.

Then they came to the straits by Lilybaeum, and saw Sicily, the three-cornered island, under which Enceladus the giant lies groaning day and night, and when he turns the earth quakes, and his breath bursts out in roaring flames from the highest cone of Aetna, above the chestnut woods. And there Charybdis caught them in its fearful coils of wave, and rolled mast-high about them, and spun them round and round ; and they could go neither back nor forward, while the whirlpool sucked them in.

And while they struggled they saw near them, on the other side of the strait, a rock stand in the water, with a peak wrapt round in clouds—a rock which no man could climb, though he had twenty hands and feet, for the stone was smooth and slippery, as if polished by man's hand ; and half-way up a misty cave looked out toward the west. And when Orpheus saw it he groaned, and struck his hands together. And " Little will it help us," he cried, " to escape the jaws of the whirlpool ; for in that cave lies Scylla, the sea-hag with a young whelp's voice ; my mother warned me of her ere we sailed away from Hellas ; she has six heads, and six long necks, and hides in that dark cleft. And from her cave she fishes for all things which pass by—for sharks, and seals, and dolphins, and all the herds of Amphitrite. And never ship's crew boasted that they came safe by her rock, for she bends her long necks down to them, and every mouth takes up

a man. And who will help us now ? For Hera and
Zeus hate us, and our ship is foul with guilt ; so we must
die, whatever befalls."

Then out of the depths came Thetis, Peleus' silver-
footed bride, for love of her gallant husband, and all her
nymphs around her ; and they played like snow-white
dolphins, diving on from wave to wave, before the ship,
and in her wake, and beside her, as dolphins play. And
they caught the ship, and guided her, and passed her on
from hand to hand, and tossed her through the billows,
as maidens toss the ball. And when Scylla stooped to
seize her, they struck back her ravening heads, and foul
Scylla whined, as a whelp whines, at the touch of their
gentle hands. But she shrank into her cave affrighted—
for all bad things shrink from good—and *Argo* leapt safe
past her, while a fair breeze rose behind. Then Thetis
and her nymphs sank down to their coral caves beneath
the sea, and their gardens of green and purple, where live
flowers bloom all the year round ; while the heroes went
on rejoicing, yet dreading what might come next.

[They rested for a time in the land of the Phaeaces,
where Alcinous, the rich sea-going king, feasted them.
Then after wandering for many a weary day in the quick-
sands of the Syrtis, near the burning shore of Africa, they
gained the open sea, and rowed toward the northward.]
At last they saw a long, steep island, and a blue peak
high among the clouds ; and they knew it for the peak of
Ida, and the famous land of Crete. And they said, " We
will land in Crete, and see Minos the just king, and all
his glory and his wealth ; at least he will treat us hospitably,
and let us fill our water-casks upon the shore."

But when they came nearer to the island they saw a
wondrous sight upon the cliffs. For on a cape to the
westward stood a giant, taller than any mountain pine,
who glittered aloft against the sky like a tower of burnished

brass. He turned and looked on all sides round him, till he saw the *Argo* and her crew ; and when he saw them he came toward them, more swiftly than the swiftest horse, leaping across the glens at a bound, and striding at one step from down to down. And when he came abreast of them he brandished his arms up and down, as a ship hoists and lowers her yards, and shouted with his brazen throat like a trumpet from off the hills, " You are pirates, you are robbers ! If you dare land here you die."

Then the heroes cried, " We are no pirates. We are all good men and true, and all we ask is food and water ; " but the giant cried the more, " You are robbers, you are pirates all ; I know you ; and if you land you shall die the death." Then he waved his arms again as a signal, and they saw the people flying inland, driving their flocks before them, while a great flame arose among the hills. Then the giant ran up a valley and vanished, and the heroes lay on their oars in fear.

But Medeia stood watching all from under her steep black brows, with a cunning smile upon her lips, and a cunning plot within her heart. At last she spoke, " I know this giant. I heard of him in the East. Hephaistos the Fire King made him in his forge in Aetna beneath the earth, and called him Talus, and gave him to Minos for a servant, to guard the coast of Crete. Thrice a day he walks round the island, and never stops to sleep ; and if strangers land he leaps into his furnace, which flames there among the hills ; and when he is red-hot he rushes on them, and burns them in his brazen hands."

Then all the heroes cried, " What shall we do, wise Medeia ? We must have water, or we die of thirst. Flesh and blood we can face fairly ; but who can face this red-hot brass ? "

" I can face red-hot brass, if the tale I hear be true.

For they say that he has but one vein in all his body, filled with liquid fire ; and that this vein is closed with a nail; but I know not where that nail is placed. But if I can get it once into these hands, you shall water your ship here in peace." Then she bade them put her on shore, and row off again, and wait what would befall.

And the heroes obeyed her unwillingly, for they were ashamed to leave her so alone ; but Jason said, " She is dearer to me than to any of you, yet I will trust her freely on shore ; she has more plots than we can dream of in the windings of that fair and cunning head." So they left the witch-maiden on the shore ; and she stood there in her beauty all alone, till the giant strode back red-hot from head to heel, while the grass hissed and smoked beneath his tread.

And when he saw the maiden alone he stopped ; and she looked boldly up into his face without moving, and began her magic song :

" Life is short, though life is sweet ; and even men of brass and fire must die. The brass must rust, the fire must cool, for time gnaws all things in their turn. Life is short, life is sweet : but sweeter to live for ever ; sweeter to live ever youthful like the Gods, who have ichor in their veins—ichor which gives life, and youth, and joy, and a bounding heart."

Then Talus said, " Who are you, strange maiden, and where is this ichor of youth ? " Then Medeia held up a flask of crystal, and said, " Here is the ichor of youth. I am Medeia the enchantress ; my sister Circe gave me this, and said, ' Go and reward Talus, the faithful servant, for his fame is gone out into all lands.' So come, and I will pour this in your veins, that you may live for ever young." And he listened to her false words, that simple Talus, and came near ; and Medeia said, " Dip yourself in the sea first, and cool yourself, lest you burn my tender hands ; then show me where the nail in your vein is, that I may pour the ichor in."

Then that simple Talus dipped himself in the sea, till it hissed, and roared, and smoked ; and came and knelt before Medeia, and showed her the secret nail. And she drew the nail out gently, but she poured no ichor in ; and instead the liquid fire spouted forth, like a stream of red-hot iron. And Talus tried to leap up, crying, " You have betrayed me, false witch-maiden ! " But she lifted up her hands before him, and sang, till he sank beneath her spell. And as he sank, his brazen limbs clanked heavily, and the earth groaned beneath his weight ; and the liquid fire ran from his heel, like a stream of lava, to the sea ; and Medeia laughed, and called to the heroes, " Come ashore, and water your ship in peace." So they came, and found the giant lying dead ; and they fell down, and kissed Medeia's feet ; and watered their ship, and took sheep and oxen, and so left that inhospitable shore.

At last, after many more adventures, they came all worn and tired by Sunium, and up the long Euboean Strait, until they saw once more Pelion, and Aphetai, and Iolcos by the sea. So they ran the ship ashore ; but they had no strength left to haul her up the beach ; and they crawled out on the pebbles, and sat down, and wept till they could weep no more. For the houses and the trees were all altered ; and all the faces which they saw were strange ; and their joy was swallowed up in sorrow, while they thought of their youth, and all their labour, and the gallant comrades they had lost.

And the people crowded round, and asked them, " Who are you, that you sit weeping here ? "

" We are the sons of your princes, who sailed out many a year ago. We went to fetch the Golden Fleece, and we have brought it, and grief therewith. Give us news of our fathers and our mothers, if any of them be left alive

on earth." Then there was shouting and laughing, and
weeping ; and all the kings came to the shore, and they
led away the heroes to their homes.

CHARLES KINGSLEY, *The Heroes*

DAEDALUS AND ICARUS

DAEDALUS, who was a famous craftsman, was detained in
the island of Crete against his will by the Cretan king,
Minos. He made wings of feathers and tried with his
son Icarus to fly home to Athens over the Aegean Sea.

> Daedalus longed to see his home again
> And hated his long exile in far Crete.
> The sea was closed. " Let the king block the land
> And sea," he cried ; " the heaven lies open still,
> There lies my way ; Minos, the king of all,
> Is not king of the air." His mind he turns
> To arts unknown and seeks inventions strange.
> Feathers he lays in order by their length,
> From smallest up to greatest, as the pipes
> That peasants play are made of reeds that slant
> In varying lengths up to a point. He binds
> The centre quills with mud, the outer ones
> With wax and gives the wing thus made a twist
> To curve it like a bird's. Then Icarus,
> His boy, who stood by laughing (unaware
> He handled his own peril) when the breeze
> Ruffled the feathers, snatched at them ; his thumb
> Softened the golden wax, and by his play
> He marred his father's wondrous work ; at last
> The final touch was laid ; then Daedalus
> Balanced his body on the wings and hung
> Amid the gusts of air and warned his son :
> " Be sure," he said, " to keep a middle course.

Fly not too low lest the waves soak your wings,
High up the sun may scorch them ; fly between.
Let not your eyes be gazing on the stars,
But follow me." He told him how to fly
Fitting his shoulders with the strange new wings,
And as he talked and worked with trembling hands
The old man's cheeks were wet with tears ; he kissed
His son for the last time, rose on his wings
And flew ahead fearing for Icarus.
Ev'n so a bird from a high nest lures forth
Her young ones to the air and urges them
To follow her. He plied his fatal craft,
Flapped his own wings, looking back at his son's.
The shepherd with his crook, the fisherman
With bending rod, the peasant leaning on
His plough beheld them flying, and amazed
Believed them gods who could thus travel through
The air. Already on the left they passed
Samos and Delos ; Paros lay behind,
Lebynthos and Calymne, haunt of bees,
When the boy, joyful at his daring flight,
Forsook his guide, and seized with mad desire
For the wide heav'n, flew up and up until
Near the fierce sun the scented wax, that held
His wings together, melted and grew soft.
With wingless shoulders he could fly no more,
But calling on his father's name he fell
Into that sea which takes its name from him.
His wretched father, childless now, called out,
" Where art thou, Icarus ? " " Where shall I seek
Thee, Icarus ? " he cried ; then saw the wings
Amid the waves and cursed what he had made.
He laid the body in a tomb ; the land
Was named from Icarus.

DORA PYM, *Readings from the Literature
of Ancient Rome*

PERSEUS AND ANDROMEDA

[AFTER many adventures Perseus, aided by the goddess Athene, who gave him winged sandals by which he could fly, a divine sword, and a polished shield, slew the loathly Gorgon, Medusa, and obtained the hat of darkness from Atlas, the giant who holds the heavens and the earth apart.

> Now at his side a wallet Perseus bore,
> With threads of yellow gold embroidered o'er ;
> Shuddering, therein he laid the fearful head,
> Lest he unwitting yet might join the dead,
> Or those he loved by sight of it be slain.[1]

On the return journey he rescued Andromeda, who was being sacrificed to appease the wrath of the Gods.]

Perseus flew up the shore of Palestine, past pleasant hills and valleys, like Argos itself, or Lacedaemon, or the fair Vale of Tempe. But the lowlands were all drowned by floods, and the highlands blasted by fire, and the hills heaved like a bubbling cauldron, before the wrath of King Poseidon, the shaker of the earth.

And Perseus feared to go inland, but flew along the shore above the sea ; and he went on all the day, and the sky was black with smoke ; and he went on all the night, and the sky was red with flame.

And at the dawn of day he looked toward the cliffs ; and at the water's edge, under a black rock, he saw a white image stand. " This," thought he, " must surely be the statue of some sea-God ; I will go near and see what kind of Gods these barbarians worship."

So he came near ; but when he came, it was no statue, but a maiden of flesh and blood ; for he could see her tresses streaming in the breeze ; and as he came closer

---

[1] From *The Doom of King Acrisius*, in *The Earthly Paradise*, by William Morris.

still, he could see how she shrank and shivered when the waves sprinkled her with cold salt spray. Her arms were spread above her head, and fastened to the rock with chains of brass ; and her head drooped on her bosom, either with sleep, or weariness, or grief. But now and then she looked up and wailed, and called her mother ; yet she did not see Perseus, for the cap of darkness was on his head.

Full of pity and indignation, Perseus drew near and looked upon the maid. Her cheeks were darker than his were, and her hair was blue-black like a hyacinth ; but Perseus thought, " I have never seen so beautiful a maiden; no, not in all our isles. Surely she is a king's daughter. Do barbarians treat their kings' daughters thus ? She is too fair, at least, to have done any wrong. I will speak to her."

And lifting the hat from his head, he flashed into her sight. She shrieked with terror, and tried to hide her face with her hair, for she could not with her hands ; but Perseus cried :

" Do not fear me, fair one ; I am a Hellen, and no barbarian. What cruel men have bound you ? But first I will set you free."

And he tore at the fetters, but they were too strong for him ; while the maiden cried :

" Touch me not ; I am accursed, devoted as a victim to the sea-Gods. They will slay you, if you dare to set me free."

" Let them try," said Perseus ; and drawing Herpé from his thigh, he cut through the brass as if it had been flax.

" Now," he said, " you belong to me, and not to these sea-Gods, whosoever they may be ! " But she only called the more on her mother.

" Why call on your mother ? She can be no mother

to have left you here. If a bird is dropped out of the nest, it belongs to the man who picks it up. If a jewel is cast by the wayside, it is his who dare win it and wear it, as I will win you and will wear you. I know now why Pallas Athene sent me hither. She sent me to gain a prize worth all my toil and more."

And he clasped her in his arms, and cried, " Where are these sea-Gods, cruel and unjust, who doom fair maids to death ? I carry the weapons of Immortals. Let them measure their strength against mine ! But tell me, maiden, who you are, and what dark fate brought you here."

And she answered, weeping :

" I am the daughter of Cepheus, King of Iopa, and my mother is Cassiopoeia of the beautiful tresses, and they called me Andromeda, as long as life was mine. And I stand bound here, hapless that I am, for the sea-monster's food, to atone for my mother's sin. For she boasted of me once that I was fairer than Atargatis, Queen of the Fishes ; so she in her wrath sent the sea-floods, and her brother the Fire King sent the earthquakes, and wasted all the land, and after the floods a monster bred of the slime, who devours all living things. And now he must devour me, guiltless though I am—me who never harmed a living thing, nor saw a fish upon the shore but I gave it life, and threw it back into the sea ; for in our land we eat no fish, for fear of Atargatis their queen. Yet the priests say that nothing but my blood can atone for a sin which I never committed."

But Perseus laughed, and said, " A sea-monster ? I have fought with worse than him : I would have faced Immortals for your sake ; how much more a beast of the sea ? "

Then Andromeda looked up at him, and new hope was kindled in her breast, so proud and fair did he stand, with one hand round her, and in the other the glittering sword. But she only sighed, and wept the more, and cried :

" Why will you die, young as you are ? Is there not death and sorrow enough in the world already ? It is noble for me to die, that I may save the lives of the whole people ; but you, better than them all, why should I slay you too ? Go you your way ; I must go mine."

But Perseus cried, " Not so ; for the Lords of Olympus, whom I serve, are the friends of the heroes, and help them on to noble deeds. Led by them, I slew the Gorgon, the beautiful horror ; and not without them do I come hither, to slay this monster with that same Gorgon's head. Yet hide your eyes when I leave you, lest the sight of it freeze you too to stone."

But the maiden answered nothing, for she could not believe his words. And then, suddenly looking up, she pointed to the sea, and shrieked :

" There he comes, with the sunrise, as they promised. I must die now. How shall I endure it ? Oh, go ! Is it not dreadful enough to be torn piecemeal, without having you to look on ? " And she tried to thrust him away.

But he said, " I go ; yet promise me one thing ere I go : that if I slay this beast you will be my wife, and come back with me to my kingdom in fruitful Argos, for I am a king's heir. Promise me, and seal it with a kiss."

Then she lifted up her face, and kissed him ; and Perseus laughed for joy, and flew upward, while Andromeda crouched trembling on the rock, waiting for what might befall.

On came the great sea-monster, coasting along like a huge black galley, lazily breasting the ripple, and stopping at times by creek or headland to watch for the laughter of girls at their bleaching, or cattle pawing on the sand-hills, or boys bathing on the beach. His great sides were fringed with clustering shells and sea-weeds, and the water gurgled in and out of his wide jaws, as he rolled along, dripping and glistening in the beams of the morning sun.

At last he saw Andromeda, and shot forward to take his prey, while the waves foamed white behind him, and before him the fish fled leaping.

Then down from the height of the air fell Perseus like a shooting star ; down to the crests of the waves, while Andromeda hid her face as he shouted ; and then there was silence for a while.

At last she looked up trembling, and saw Perseus springing toward her ; and instead of the monster a long black rock, with the sea rippling quietly round it.

Who then so proud as Perseus, as he leapt back to the rock, and lifted his fair Andromeda in his arms, and flew with her to the cliff-top, as a falcon carries a dove ?

Who so proud as Perseus, and who so joyful as all the Aethiop people ? For they had stood watching the monster from the cliffs, wailing for the maiden's fate. And already a messenger had gone to Cepheus and Cassiopoeia, where they sat in sackcloth and ashes on the ground in the innermost palace chambers, awaiting their daughter's end. And they came, and all the city with them, to see the wonder, with songs and with dances, with cymbals and harps, and received their daughter back again, as one alive from the dead.

[And Perseus married the fair Andromeda, and then went home to Argos, and reigned there for many a year.]

When they died, the ancients say, Athene took them up into the sky, with Cepheus and Cassiopoeia. And there on starlight nights you may see them shining still ; Cepheus with his kingly crown, and Cassiopoeia in her ivory chair, plaiting her star-spangled tresses, and Perseus with the Gorgon's head, and fair Andromeda beside him,

D

spreading her long white arms across the heaven, as she stood when chained to the stone for the monster. All night long they shine, for a beacon to wandering sailors; but all day they feast with the Gods, on the still blue peaks of Olympus.

CHARLES KINGSLEY, The Heroes

PERSEPHONE

PERSEPHONE was the daughter of the goddess Demeter, or Ceres, and when she was gathering flowers in the Sicilian meadows Pluto, the god of the Underworld, came with his chariot and carried her off to his kingdom down below.

Persephone through meadows once was straying
    With girls, her wonted playmates, when she found
A shady spot a waterfall was spraying
    That leapt from lofty hills to valley ground.
There all the colours Nature knows were gleaming,
    With countless flowers the earth was painted bright.
" Come, girls," the maiden cried, " and cease your dreaming.
    We'll fill our arms with blossoms, our delight."
Their girlish hearts were filled with joy of plunder,
    So hard they worked it made the work seem less,
One baskets filled of osiers woven under,
    One fills her arms and one her loosened dress,
One seeks the violets blue, another golden
    Kingcups, another plucks the poppies frail,
By hyacinths and amaranth are holden
    Yet others, thyme they pick and clover pale,
And cassia, and most of all sweet roses,
    And nameless flow'rs; the maid Persephone
Wanders afar in her desire of posies,
    White lilies, slender crocuses; none see

Their mistress go ; of all the girls none follow,
  But she is seen, and swift from realms below
Comes Pluto, captures her and straight the hollow
  Road underground lies open and they go,
Drawn by his great black horses, hardly bearing
  The strange and unaccustomed light of day.
She cried aloud and screamed, her long robes tearing,
  " My darling mother, I am snatched away."
But now, her basket full of flow'rs, each maiden
  " Persephone ! " calls, " Come to your gifts, come !"
Wretched, they beat their breasts, the hills are laden
  With crying ; she they call alone is dumb.

               DORA PYM, *Readings from the Literature*
                      of Ancient Rome

THE SEARCH FOR PERSEPHONE

[IN the following passage Ceres describes her search for
the missing Persephone.]

             Child, when thou wert gone,
I envied human wives, and nested birds,
Yea, the cubb'd lioness ; went in search of thee
Thro' many a palace, many a cot . . .
I climb'd on all the cliffs of all the seas,
And ask'd the waves that moan about the world
" Where ? do ye make your moaning for my child?"
And round from all the world the voices came
" We know not, and we know not why we moan."
" Where ? " and I stared from every eagle-peak,
I thridded the black heart of all the woods,
I peer'd thro' tomb and cave, and in the storms
Of Autumn swept across the city, and heard
The murmur of their temples chanting me,
Me, me, the desolate Mother !   " Where ? "

[At last she hears that Persephone has been carried off by Pluto to become " the Bride of Darkness."]

Then I, Earth-Goddess, cursed the Gods of Heaven.
I would not mingle with their feasts ; to me
Their nectar smack'd of hemlock on the lips,
Their rich ambrosia tasted aconite. . . .
My quick tears kill'd the flower, my ravings hush'd
The bird, and lost in utter grief I fail'd
To send my life thro' olive-yard and vine
And golden grain, my gifts to helpless man.
Rain-rotten died the wheat, the barley-spears
Were hollow-husk'd, the leaf fell, and the sun,
Pale at my grief, drew down before his time
Sickening, and Aetna kept her winter snow.
    Then He, the brother of this Darkness, He
Who still is highest, glancing from his height
On earth a fruitless fallow, when he miss'd
The wonted steam of sacrifice, the praise
And prayer of men, decreed that thou should'st dwell
For nine white moons of each whole year with me,
Three dark ones in the shadow with thy King.
    Once more the reaper in the gleam of dawn
Will see me by the landmark far away,
Blessing his field, or seated in the dusk
Of even, by the lonely threshing-floor,
Rejoicing in the harvest and the grange.

LORD TENNYSON , Demeter and Persephone

ATALANTA'S RACE

THE town of King Schoeneus lay bathed in a flood of April sunshine, when a noble young huntsman, tired of his sport in the deep forest, wandered through its un-guarded gateway. It surprised him to find the streets deserted, but before long he discovered the reason. Towards one quarter of the city crowds were streaming with grave faces and many anxious words. Filled with curiosity young Milanion joined the throng, and presently found himself on an open space where tiers of seats looked down on a race-course that curved round the turning-post at its middle point. Beneath a canopy King Schoeneus sat enthroned in the midst of his councillors, while close by his throne stood a golden image of the sun-god Apollo, and a silver image of the goddess of the moon, Diana. A brazen altar was there, and at the side of it a giant-like man held a sword, against whose shining steel was laid a wreath of yellow flowers. A herald in gold and crimson array was also on the scene, with his horn even now raised to his lips.

But it was the sight of the runners in the coming race that most interested Milanion. There were but two of them, bending foot to foot at the starting-point. The one, a young man of a slim, well-knit figure, his crisp locks crowned with a small golden circlet, and in his hand an olive branch that betokened his prayers for a happy, peaceful ending to the contest, was trembling with excitement, and his eyes were bent longingly and anxiously upon his rival in the race. Unlike the first, the other combatant showed a calmness that would have been remarkable in any man facing such an ordeal, but was the more so in that it was here displayed by a young girl ! She stood there, tall and supple, her grey eyes untroubled, and her smooth, white brow free from any trace of anxiety.

It was now sundown, and as the great fiery globe dropped beneath the western sky-line, the herald blew a loud blast on his horn, and instantly a little cloud of dust rose from the track down which man and maiden sprang from the line. Their course was swift as the wind. Side by side they rounded the turning-post at the farther end, and when the onlookers saw that they were still abreast, and the race already half run, cries of joy arose, and the crowds shouted words of encouragement, all directed towards the young man. Milanion had scarcely time to wonder why no one wished the girl well before the race was over. Piqued by the cheering that was given to her opponent, she caught up her fluttering robe, with an easy grace outran him, and ere he could dash forward she had laid her fingers on the goal! Her cheeks were not over-flushed, nor her eyes sparkling with triumph; quietly, and with a bearing that was less proud than at the outset of the race, she turned away from the winning-post.

And then Milanion understood why the people had wished the young man to out-strip her, for, stopping short when he saw the maiden reach the goal, the vanquished runner gazed at her with dull, dim eyes, and as she disappeared he stifled a groan of despair. He dropped on his knees before the huge-limbed swordsman; the flowers were shaken off the sword, the naked steel flashed in the air, and the poor young fellow lay dead beneath its stroke.

The crowd broke up silently, and scattered in little groups that sought to forget the sad end of the race by busying themselves with talk of other matters. Milanion saw from the manner in which they took it that such a sight as that afternoon's was not unusual in their city, so stepping up to an old man he begged to know why death was the penalty for losing the race, and whether the young girl was mortal or, as he judged from her beauty, a goddess upon earth.

"Stranger," cried the old man with a blaze of anger, "I pray that she who runs these wicked races may be taken from our earth! She is no goddess, forsooth, but the daughter of King Schoeneus. Her upbringing was rough, and in that, methinks, lies some excuse for the hard heart she shows now.

"When she was born, her father was wroth to have a girl child, and ordered his servants to take the infant to the woods, and leave it there to perish. (Ah! no wonder the daughter of such a man is cold-hearted, and dreads to marry lest her husband be unkind as her father.) Well, Atalanta, the infant, was, happily, befriended in the forest; at first, they say, by a great shaggy bear, who, instead of hugging the life out of the little one, nursed her amongst a litter of shapeless cubs, and when one day this mother bear was killed by our woodmen, one of them picked up the child, and had her reared in his cottage. She grew to be a true daughter of the woods, skilled with her bow and arrows, while in swiftness of foot there is no man in the country—none, perchance, in the world—to equal her.

"Years passed, and the gods punished King Schoeneus for his unfatherly act by sending him no other child, so that he came to pine sadly for the daughter whom he had long ago cast from him. At length Atalanta happened to come to the city, and, her strange history being noised abroad, the King heard of her, recognized his child by some sign, and with tears of joy welcomed her to his palace.

"Schoeneus is now a kind-hearted, gentle king, who would fain see his daughter wed happily; but she, proud maid, has vowed to the goddess Diana that whoso wishes to make her his bride must first run a race with her. If the suitor wins the race, he wins also his bride, but if he fails to reach the winning-post before Atalanta, then must he forfeit his life on the spot. Many a gallant man has risked his life, and lost it, for love of the fleet-footed girl.

"Thine eyes are shining, stranger, as though thou

wouldst make the trial thyself! Nay, I implore thee, dream not of wedding Atalanta. Her nimble feet would outstrip thee as easily as they sped past that young knight to-day, for all that he ran more swiftly than her former suitors. The goddess Diana herself is on the maiden's side."

Milanion could not banish from his thoughts the story of Atalanta or the remembrance of her supple beauty. He went back to the forest, but found that hunting had lost its charms ; he wandered through Argive cities, and won great renown in the public games ; but still he was dissatisfied, and saw in his mind another race-course, where he would have a white-footed girl to compete with, and where the prize would be infinitely dearer to him than any that he had hitherto contended for.

A month had not passed before he entered King Schoeneus' city a second time. He found the course prepared for another race, and the next evening saw one more suitor worsted by Atalanta, and slain accordingly beneath the statue of Diana. Yet Milanion thought less of the hapless man's fate than of that chance of gaining bliss untold for which life after life had been thrown away. He knew now that he was hopelessly in love with Atalanta, and that nothing could stop his longing to enter the lists. He must go in and win her—or die. Was he as swift as she ? He hardly dared hope so, unsurpassed though he had proved in the Argive races. But without her, life was worthless and empty ; and at last he determined that he would at least end his misery by pitting himself against her.

After a long, restless night he rose, and roamed about the town until the hour arrived at which Schoeneus took his seat upon the throne of ivory in the market-place to give judgment to his people and hear their requests. The anxious face of the young stranger as he pressed

forward towards the King's throne told its own story.
Too often had the townsfolk seen a gallant lad present
himself before the King to ask the fatal favour of racing
with the unconquerable maiden.

Schoeneus himself guessed the answer he would receive
as he inquired if it were to gain this permission that the
unknown youth stood before him.

" It is, O King," replied the other, " and I trust it will
be granted me to make the attempt. Fear not that I
who seek the hand of Atalanta am of unworthy family.
King Amphidamus is my father, and his crown is mine
after him."

" Nay, then, Prince," said Schoeneus very earnestly,
" thou shouldst not throw away thy life, which is dear
to a whole kingdom. Believe me, the goddess Diana has
given my daughter a fleetness of foot that no man can
equal, and if thou art beaten in the race no power on earth
can save thee from the sword. Already I fear the anger
of the gods for all the deaths that lie at our door, and I
beg thee, for mine own sake as well as thine, to forego
this mad enterprise."

But Milanion stoutly refused to retire. He waited
only to know how soon the contest might take place.
Why not to-day, he said—the sooner his fate was decided
the less suspense he would have to suffer. But the King
would not hear of such haste. He declared that, since
Milanion insisted on the race, it would be held in a
month's time, and not a day sooner. For that month
he invited the young man to be his guest at the palace—
an invitation which Milanion, however, did not choose
to accept, dreading perhaps that to see Atalanta in the
interval might unnerve him for the trial. He told the
King that he preferred to wander from one shrine to
another, making what vows he could, to gain aid from the
gods in this issue of life and death ; and he must also

return to Argos to see his friends again—it might be for the last time.

And so with expressions of goodwill on either side, mingled with sad forebodings, King Schoeneus bade Milanion farewell.

On the shore of Argolis stood a temple to Venus, the sea-born goddess. Her image was placed between the pillars that marked the top of a small flight of steps, up which the blue waves crept twice a day until they kissed the white feet of the marble goddess. The temple was but a tiny place, yet nowhere in Greece could you have found a richer store of treasures than when you passed through the lines of myrtle-trees and pushed ajar the great brass doors that guarded the landward side of Venus' shrine.

It was hither that Milanion brought mirrors fit for the very goddess of beauty to gaze in, carved bowls of the rarest handiwork, and bales of soft Indian silks. With these offerings he came to pray the goddess of the temple for her help in the contest with Diana's maiden.

" Aid me, O Queen of Love, and grant me victory over thy fair rebel," he cried, " for never has man loved Atalanta as I !   Until the day when I must go to meet my death, I will not leave thy temple unless thou sendest me a token of thy favour. Oh ! help me, Venus, to win the fleet-footed maiden to be thy servant and my bride."

True to his word, Milanion waited beside the altar of the Goddess of Love. Many an hour passed ; the gold of sunset changed to the deep blue shades of a summer evening ; the midnight hymn floated from the inner court, where a sweet-faced band of maidens clustered beneath the flickering torches ; the little waves rose rippling over the steps beneath him ; but the prince noted nothing—not though the rising sea tossed its light spray against his face did he move from his station beneath the image of fair Venus. And in time he got his answer.

Between the fading of night and the dawning of a new day, the South grew shining bright with the passage of a wonderful cloud that lit up sea and sky as it floated on the crests of the advancing billows. Venus was on her way to her temple ! Milanion bent his head, and threw his mantle across his eyes as the dazzling vision drew near and the fragrance of the heavenly queen was wafted from the cloud of mist in which she was veiled.

A sweet voice, clear as a bell, told him that his whole-hearted cry to Venus had been heard, and that the goddess would aid him to win the maiden from Diana, who frowned upon the weaknesses of love. On the steps of the altar he would find three golden apples, dropped from the white hand of Venus herself. These he must carry with him to the race ; let him but roll one of them past Atalanta and the young girl would not fail to turn aside in pursuit of it, so lovely was the fruit and so irresistible its charm.

With a parting reminder that she who had done so much for him would look for worship from Milanion and his bride in the happy future, the clouded figure glided from the sea-worn steps, where in the grey dawn gleamed Atalanta's lure—three marvellous, heaven-sent apples of beaten gold.

At length the day has come when Milanion stands beside the white-footed maiden upon the course, sand-strewn for their race, while crowds have gathered, awaiting the wonted spectacle of a fresh suitor's defeat and death. " But does not this young prince bear himself confidently ? " murmur the bystanders. " Those who aforetime entered the lists with Atalanta looked wan and anxious ; this man has a glow of joyous hope on his face and holds himself as one who means to win."

What others were remarking was not unnoticed by the girl at Milanion's side. She felt his eyes rest on her with no pleading look of farewell, but full of the gentleness that comes of assured strength. With a sudden start of surprise she wondered whether, since he meant to succeed, he might not do so ; then she went on to think how sad a fate it would be for such a gallant prince to be slain at the end of the course. She would be sorry, would she not, when she won ?

Just then the trumpet gave the signal, and, throwing aside what scruples were gathering in her mind, she sped forward, determined to play her part, and do her best to outstrip the man who was racing for dear love of her. She darted past Milanion so swiftly that the crowd shouted his case was hopeless, when, lo ! a round golden apple was flung from his hand, and rolled past Atalanta some distance out of the track. The words that Venus had spoken were true ; the swift-footed maiden was tempted aside to pick up the enticing prize, and while she swerved from the course, Milanion gained the lead.

To regain the advantage, Atalanta pressed on more eagerly than before. The bow that she was wont to carry in her hand, as a sign that she was devoted to the huntress-maiden, Diana, was dropped when she stooped to seize the golden apple of Venus, and at the same time three arrows slipped from the quiver slung across her shoulder. Yet she prayed her patron goddess to remember her handmaid ; and Diana still counted the maiden hers, and lent her the greater swiftness of foot. Milanion's hand was on the turning post when Atalanta sprang round the bend of the track in front of him.

Another golden ball rolled glittering across the sandy path, and lay, a tempting sight, out of the course, but not out of the maiden's sight. She hesitated, thought perchance of the ease with which she had but now gained on her rival, and then allowed herself to turn aside to secure this second treasure. Both apples she held in the folds of her robe, and with it well gathered about her, she flew on her way till once more she was abreast of Milanion. The two runners were now fast approaching the goal ; the crowds stood motionless with excitement, for though all saw that the girl was the swifter of the two, it seemed just possible that Milanion might once again tempt her to leave the course. And this was, indeed, the case. He flung the third apple across her path, and the wonderful charm of the fruit overcame the white-footed Atalanta as she saw it gleam before her eyes. She had time, she cried to herself, to snatch it up like the others, and still to come first to the goal, and win the victory that meant, alas ! death to the noblest suitor against whom she had ever contended.

She darted aside, and raised the prized apple from the dust. Then she lightly turned to speed towards the winning-post. But what means that hoarse roar of applause, that deafening shout of joy from the crowd that a moment ago was breathlessly silent ? She sees as she lifts her eyes to the goal that her rival already stands there ! He has won the race, and escaped death ; he has gained Atalanta as his bride. A few faltering steps, and she is at the end of the course, and as Milanion's strong arms are thrown round her, she is glad at heart that he has proved himself the victor !

M. G. EDGAR, *Stories from the Earthly Paradise*

THESEUS

HOW HE LIFTED THE STONE

ONCE upon a time there was a princess in Troezene, Aithra, the daughter of Pittheus the king. She had one fair son, named Theseus, the bravest lad in all the land ; and

Aithra never smiled but when she looked at him, for her husband had forgotten her, and lived far away. And she used to go up to the mountain above Troezene, to the temple of Poseidon, and sit there all day looking out across the bay to the purple peaks of Aegina and the Attic shore beyond. And when Theseus was full fifteen years old she took him up with her to the temple, and into the thickets of the grove which grew in the temple-yard. And she led him to a tall plane-tree, beneath whose shade grew arbutus, and lentisk, and purple heather-bushes. And there she sighed, and said, "Theseus, my son, go into that thicket, and you will find at the plane-tree foot a great flat stone; lift it, and bring me what lies underneath."

Then Theseus pushed his way in through the thick bushes, and saw that they had not been moved for many a year. And searching among their roots he found a great flat stone, all overgrown with ivy, and acanthus, and moss. He tried to lift it, but he could not. And he tried till the sweat ran down his brow from heat, and the tears from his eyes for shame; but all was of no avail. And at last he came back to his mother, and said, "I have found the stone, but I cannot lift it; nor do I think that any man could in all Troezene."

His mother sighed, and said, "The Gods wait long; but they are just at last. Let it be for another year: The day may come when you will be a stronger man than lives in all Troezene." Then she took him by the hand, and went into the temple and prayed, and came down again with Theseus to her home.

And when a full year was past she led Theseus up again to the temple, and bade him lift the stone; but he could not. Then she sighed, and said the same words again, and went down, and came again the next year; but Theseus could not lift the stone then, nor the year after; and he longed to ask his mother the meaning of that stone, and what might lie underneath it ; but her face was so sad that he had not the heart to ask.

So he said to himself, " The day shall surely come when I will lift that stone, though no man in Troezene can." And in order to grow strong he spent all his days in wrestling, and boxing, and hurling, and taming horses, and hunting the boar and the bull, and coursing goats and deer among the rocks ; till upon all the mountains there was no hunter so swift as Theseus ; and he killed Phaia, the wild sow of Crommyon, which wasted all the land ; till all the people said, " Surely the Gods are with the lad."

And when his eighteenth year was past, Aithra led him up again to the temple, and said, " Theseus, lift the stone this day, or never know who you are." And Theseus went into the thicket, and stood over the stone, and tugged at it ; and it moved. Then his spirit swelled within him, and he said, " If I break my heart in my body, it shall up." And he tugged at it once more, and lifted it, and rolled it over with a shout.

And when he looked beneath it, on the ground lay a sword of bronze, with a hilt of glittering gold, and by it a pair of golden sandals ; and he caught them up, and burst through the bushes like a wild boar, and leapt to his mother, holding them high above his head.

But when she saw them she wept long in silence, hiding her fair face in her shawl ; and Theseus stood by wondering, and wept also, he knew not why. And when she was tired of weeping she lifted up her head, and laid her finger on her lips, and said, " Hide them in your bosom, Theseus my son, and come with me where we can look down upon the sea."

Then they went outside the sacred wall, and looked down over the bright blue sea ; and Aithra said :

" Do you see this land at our feet ? "

And he said, " Yes ; this is Troezene, where I was born and bred."

And she said, " It is but a little land, barren and rocky, and looks towards the bleak north-east. Do you see that land beyond ? "

" Yes ; that is Attica, where the Athenian people dwell."

" That is a fair land and large, Theseus my son ; a land of olive-oil and honey, the joy of Gods and men. What would you do, son Theseus, if you were king of such a land ? "

Theseus stood astonished, as he looked across the broad bright sea ; then his heart grew great within him, and he said, " If I were king of such a land I would rule it wisely and well in wisdom and in might, that when I died all men might weep over my tomb, and cry, ' Alas for the shepherd of his people ! ' "

And Aithra smiled, and said, " Take, then, the sword and the sandals, and go to Aegeus, king of Athens, and say to him, ' The stone is lifted, but whose is the pledge beneath ? ' Then show him the sword and the sandals, and take what the Gods shall send."

CHARLES KINGSLEY, The Heroes (adapted)

THE JOURNEY TO ATHENS

THOUGH it would have been easier to hire a swift ship and sail across the bay to Athens, Theseus chose to go by land, for, as he said to himself, " I will win honour and renown, and do such deeds that Aegeus shall be proud of me. I will go by land, and into the mountains, and round by the way of the isthmus. Perhaps there I may hear of brave adventures, and do something which shall win my father's love."

So he went by land, and away into the mountains, with

his father's sword upon his thigh, till he came to the Spider mountains, where the glens run downward from one peak in the midst, as the rays spread in the spider's web. And he went up into the gloomy glens, between the furrowed marble walls, till the lowland grew blue beneath his feet and the clouds drove damp about his head.

But he went up and up for ever, through the spider's web of glens, till he could see the narrow gulfs spread below him, north and south, and east and west; black cracks half-choked with mists, and above all a dreary down.

But over that down he must go, for there was no road right or left; so he toiled on through bog and brake, till he came to a pile of stones. And on the stones a man was sitting, wrapt in a bearskin cloak. The head of the bear served him for a cap, and its teeth grinned white around his brows; and the feet were tied about his throat, and their claws shone white upon his chest. And when he saw Theseus he rose, and laughed till the glens rattled.

" And who art thou, fair fly, who hast walked into the spider's web ? " But Theseus walked on steadily, and made no answer; but he thought, " Is this some robber ? and has an adventure come already to me ? " But the strange man laughed louder than ever, and said :

" Bold fly, know you not that these glens are the web from which no fly ever finds his way out again, and this down the spider's house, and I the spider who suck the flies ? Come hither, and let me feast upon you; for it is of no use to run away, so cunning a web has my father Hephaistos spread for me, when he made these clefts in the mountains, through which no man finds his way home."

But Theseus came on steadily, and asked :

F

" And what is your name among men, bold spider ? and where are your spider's fangs ? "

Then the strange man laughed again :

" My name is Periphetes, the son of Hephaistos, but men call me Corynetes the club-bearer ; and here is my spider's fang." And he lifted from off the stones at his side a mighty club of bronze.

" This my father gave me, and forged it himself in the roots of the mountain ; and with it I pound all proud flies till they give out their fatness and their sweetness. So give me up that gay sword of yours, and your mantle, and your golden sandals, lest I pound you, and by ill-luck you die."

But Theseus wrapt his mantle round his left arm quickly, in hard folds, from his shoulder to his hand, and drew his sword, and rushed upon the club-bearer, and the club-bearer rushed on him.

Thrice he struck at Theseus, and made him bend under the blows like a sapling ; but Theseus guarded his head with his left arm, and the mantle which was wrapt around it.

And thrice Theseus sprang upright after the blow, like a sapling when the storm is past ; and he stabbed at the club-bearer with his sword, but the loose folds of the bearskin saved him.

Then Theseus grew mad, and closed with him, and caught him by the throat, and they fell and rolled over together ; but when Theseus rose up from the ground the club-bearer lay still at his feet.

Then Theseus took his club and his bearskin, and left him to the kites and crows, and went on his journey.

And he went towards the Isthmus till he could see both the seas and the citadel of Corinth towering high above all the land ; and there in a pine-wood, where the Isthmus was narrowest and the road ran between high rocks, he met Sinis. There he sat upon a stone by the wayside, with a young fir-tree for a club across his knees, and a cord laid ready by his side ; and over his head, upon the fir-tops, hung the bones of murdered men.

Then Theseus shouted to him, for he had learned of him from some shepherds, " Holla, thou valiant pine-bender, hast thou two fir-trees left for me ? "

And Sinis leapt to his feet, and answered, pointing to the bones above his head, " My larder has grown empty lately, so I have two fir-trees ready for thee." And he rushed on Theseus, lifting his club, and Theseus rushed upon him.

Then they hammered together till the greenwoods rang ; but the metal was tougher than the pine, and Sinis' club broke right across, as the bronze came down upon it. Then Theseus heaved up another mighty stroke, and smote Sinis down upon his face ; and knelt upon his back, and bound him with his own cord, and said, " As thou hast done to others, so shall it be done to thee." Then he bent down two young fir-trees, and bound Sinis between them for all his struggling and his prayers ; and let them go, and ended Sinis, and went on, leaving him to the hawks and crows.

Then he went over the hills, keeping close along the sea, till he came to the cliffs of Sciron, and the narrow path between the mountain and the sea. And there he saw Sciron sitting by a fountain, at the edge of the cliff. On his knees was a mighty club ; and he had barred the path with stones, so that every one must stop who came up.

Theseus shouted to him, and said, " Holla, thou tortoise-feeder, do thy feet need washing to-day ? "

And Sciron leapt to his feet, and answered :

" My tortoise is empty and hungry, and my feet need washing to-day." And he stood before his barrier, and lifted up his club in both hands.

Then Theseus rushed upon him ; and sore was the battle upon the cliff, for when Sciron felt the weight of the bronze club, he dropt his own, and closed with Theseus, and tried to hurl him by main force over the cliff. But Theseus was a wary wrestler, and dropt his own club, and caught him by the throat and by the knee, and forced him back against the wall of stones, and crushed him up against them, till his breath was almost gone. And Sciron cried panting, " Loose me, and I will let thee pass." But Theseus answered, " I must not pass till I have made the rough way smooth " ; and he forced him back against the wall till it fell, and Sciron rolled head over heels.

Then Theseus lifted him up all bruised, and said, " Come hither and wash my feet." And he drew his sword and sat down by the well, and said, " Wash my feet, or I cut you piecemeal."

And Sciron washed his feet trembling ; and when it was done, Theseus rose, and cried, " As thou hast done to others, so shall it be done to thee. Go feed thy tortoise thyself " ; and he kicked him over the cliff into the sea.

Then Theseus went a long day's journey into the Attic land, and on his right hand was the sea always, and Salamis, with its island cliffs, and the sacred strait of the sea-fight, where afterwards the Persians fled before the Greeks ; and towards evening he came to the sacred city of Eleusis, where he wrestled with and killed King Kerkuon and took an oath of the people that they would serve him as their king.

Next morning he went away across the plain, and as he was skirting the Vale of Cephisus, along the foot of lofty Parnes, a very tall and strong man came down to meet him, dressed in rich garments. On his arm were golden bracelets, and round his neck a collar of jewels ; and he came forward, bowing courteously, and held out both his hands, and spoke :

" Welcome, fair youth, to these mountains ; happy am I to have met you ! For what greater pleasure to a good man than to entertain strangers ? But I see you are weary. Come up to my castle, and rest yourself awhile. Come up with me, and eat the best of venison, and drink the rich red wine, and sleep upon my famous bed, of which all travellers say they never saw the like. For whatsoever the stature of my guest, however tall or short, that bed fits him to a hair, and he sleeps on it as he never slept before." And he laid hold on Theseus' hands, and would not let him go.

Theseus wished to go forwards ; but he was ashamed to seem churlish to so hospitable a man ; and he was curious to see that wondrous bed ; and besides, he was hungry and weary : yet he shrank from the man, he knew not why ; for, though his voice was gentle and fawning, it was dry and husky like a toad's ; and though his eyes were gentle, they were dull and cold like stones. But he consented, and went with the man up a glen which led from the road toward the peaks of Parnes, under the dark shadow of the cliffs.

And as they went up, the glen grew narrower, and the cliffs higher and darker, and beneath them a torrent roared, half seen between bare limestone crags. And around them was neither tree nor bush, while from the white peaks of Parnes the snow-blasts swept down the glen, cutting and chilling, till a horror fell on Theseus as he looked round at that doleful place. And he asked at last, " Your castle stands, it seems, in a dreary region ? "

" Yes ; but once within it, hospitality makes all things cheerful. But who are these ? " and he looked back, and Theseus also ; and far below, along the road which they had left, came a string of laden asses, and merchants walking by them, watching their ware.

"Ah, poor souls ! ' said the stranger. " Well for them that I looked back and saw them ! And well for me too, for I shall have the more guests at my feast. Wait awhile till I go down and call them, and we will eat and drink together the live-long night. Happy am I, to whom Heaven sends so many guests at once ! "

And he ran back down the hill, waving his hand and shouting to the merchants, while Theseus went slowly up the steep pass.

But as he went up he met an aged man, who had been gathering driftwood in the torrent-bed. He laid down his faggot in the road, and was trying to lift it again to his shoulder. And when he saw Theseus, he called to him, and said :

" O fair youth, help me up with my burden, for my limbs are stiff and weak with years."

Then Theseus lifted the burden on his back. And the old man blest him, and then looked earnestly upon him, and said :

" Who are you, fair youth, and wherefore travel you this doleful road ? "

" Who I am my parents know ; but I travel this doleful road because I have been invited by a hospitable man, who promises to feast me, and to make me sleep upon I know not what wondrous bed."

Then the old man clapped his hands together and cried : " Know, fair youth, that you are going to torment and to death, for he who met you (I will requite your kindness by another) is a robber and a murderer of men. Whatsoever stranger he meets he entices him hither to death ; and as for this bed of which he speaks, truly it fits all comers, yet none ever rose alive off it save me."

" Why ? " asked Theseus, astonished.

" Because, if a man be too tall for it, he lops his limbs till they be short enough, and if he be too short, he stretches his limbs till they be long enough ; but me only he spared, seven weary years agone ; for I alone of all fitted his bed exactly, so he spared me, and made me his slave. And once I was a wealthy merchant, and dwelt in brazen-gated Thebes ; but now I hew wood and draw water for him, the torment of all mortal men. Procrustes the stretcher he is called. Flee from him, for he will have no pity on your youth. Yet whither will you flee ? The cliffs are steep, and who can climb them ? And there is no other road."

But Theseus laid his hand upon the old man's mouth, and said, " There is no need to flee "; and he turned to go down the pass.

" Do not tell him that I have warned you, or he will kill me by some evil death "; and the old man screamed after him down the glen ; but Theseus strode on in his wrath.

And he said to himself, " This is an ill-ruled land ; when shall I have done ridding it of monsters ? " And as he spoke, Procrustes came up the hill, and all the merchants with him, smiling and talking gaily. And when he saw Theseus, he cried, " Ah, fair young guest, have I kept you too long waiting ? "

But Theseus answered, " The man who stretches his guests upon a bed and hews off their hands and feet, what shall be done to him, when right is done throughout the land ? "

Then Procrustes' countenance changed, and his cheeks grew as green as a lizard, and he felt for his sword in haste ; but Theseus leapt on him, and cried :

" Is this true, my host, or is it false ? " and he clasped Procrustes round waist and elbow, so that he could not draw his sword.

" Is this true, my host, or is it false ? " But Procrustes answered never a word.

Then Theseus flung him from him, and lifted up his dreadful club ; and before Procrustes could strike him he had struck, and felled him to the ground. He stript him of his gold ornaments, and went up to his house, and found there great wealth and treasure, which he had stolen from the passers-by. And he called the people of the country, whom Procrustes had spoiled a long time, and parted the spoil among them, and went down the mountains, and away.

At length he came to Athens, and all the people ran out to see him ; for his fame had gone before him, and every one knew of his mighty deeds ; and when he had cleansed the King's palace of that evil brood, his cousins and the dark witch-maiden Medeia, the sword and the sandals revealed him as the King's son.

CHARLES KINGSLEY, *The Heroes* (adapted)

THE SLAYING OF THE MINOTAUR

THESEUS stayed with his father all the winter ; and when the spring equinox drew near, all the Athenians grew sad and silent, and Theseus saw it, and asked the reason ; but no one would answer him a word. Then he went to his father, and asked him ; but Aegeus turned away his face and wept. But at length he learned that a messenger had come to demand the tribute of seven young men and seven maidens which the city must pay to Minos, King of Crete. For Minos had sent his son to Athens to the games, and he had overcome all the Greeks in the sports, so that the people honoured him as a hero. But when Aegeus saw his valour, he envied him, and plotted against his life, and basely slew him, no man knows how or where. Yet Aegeus said that it was the young men who had killed him from envy, because he had conquered them in the games. But Minos came and avenged him, and would not depart till Athens had promised him this tribute chosen from among the noble families in the city. And it was said that these youths and maidens were devoured by the Minotaur, a frightful monster which Minos kept in a wonderful labyrinth, the work of the cunning Daedalus.

And while they were drawing lots for the youths and maidens who were to sail to that doleful fate, Theseus strode into the midst and cried :

" Here is a youth who needs no lot. I myself will be one of the seven."

And as they went down to the black-sailed ship, the people followed them lamenting. But Theseus whispered to his companions, " Have hope, for the monster is not immortal. Where are Periphetes, and Sinis, and Sciron, and all whom I have slain ? " Then their hearts were comforted a little ; but they wept as they went on board, and the cliffs rang with their lamentation as they sailed on toward their deaths in Crete.

And when they came to Crete they were brought to the palace of Minos, the great king, to whom Zeus himself taught laws ; and when Theseus stood before Minos they looked each other in the face. Then Minos bade take them to prison, and cast them to the monster one by one, that the death of his son might be avenged. Then Theseus cried :

" A boon, O Minos ! Let me be thrown first to the beast. For I came hither for that very purpose, of my own will, and not by lot."

" Who art thou, then, brave youth ? "

" I am the son of him whom of all men thou hatest most, Aegeus the King of Athens, and I am come here to end this matter."

And Minos pondered awhile, looking steadfastly at him, and he thought, "The lad means to atone by his own death for his father's sin "; and he answered at last mildly :

" Go back in peace, my son. It is a pity that one so brave should die."

But Theseus said, " I have sworn that I will not go back till I have seen the monster face to face."

And at that Minos frowned, and said, " Then thou shalt see him ; take the madman away."

And they led Theseus away into prison, with the other youths and maidens.

But Ariadne, Minos' daughter, saw him, as she came out of her white stone hall ; and she loved him for his courage and his majesty, and said, " Shame that such a youth should die ! "   And by night she went down to the prison, and told him all her heart ; and said :

" Flee down to your ship at once, for I have bribed the guards before the door. Flee, you and all your friends, and go back in peace to Greece ; and take me, take me with you ! for I dare not stay after you are gone ; for my father will kill me miserably, if he knows what I have done."

And Theseus stood silent awhile ; for he was astonished and confounded by her beauty : but at last he said, " I cannot go home in peace, till I have seen and slain this Minotaur, and avenged the deaths of the youths and maidens, and put an end to the terrors of my land."

" And will you kill the Minotaur ?   How, then ? "

" I know not, nor do I care : but he must be strong if he is too strong for me."

Then she loved him all the more, and said, " But when you have killed him, how will you find your way out of the labyrinth ? "

" I know not, neither do I care : but it must be a

strange road, if I do not find it out before I have eaten up the monster's carcase."

Then she loved him all the more, and said :

" Fair youth, you are too bold ; but I can help you, weak as I am. I will give you a sword, and with that, perhaps, you may slay the beast ; and a clue of thread, and by that, perhaps, you may find your way out again. Only promise me that if you escape safe you will take me home with you to Greece ; for my father will surely kill me, if he knows what I have done."

Then Theseus laughed, and said, " Am I not safe enough now ? " And he hid the sword in his bosom, and rolled up the clue in his hand ; and then he swore to Ariadne, and fell down before her, and kissed her hands and her feet ; and she wept over him a long while, and then went away ; and Theseus lay down and slept sweetly.

And when evening came, the guards came in and led him away to the labyrinth.

And he went down into that doleful gulf, through winding paths among the rocks, under caverns, and arches, and galleries, and over heaps of fallen stone. And he turned on the left hand, and on the right hand, and went up and down, till his head was dizzy ; but all the while he held his clue. For when he went in he had fastened it to a stone, and left it to unroll out of his hand as he went on ; and it lasted him till he met the Minotaur, in a narrow chasm between black cliffs.

And when he saw him he stopped awhile, for he had never seen so strange a beast. His body was a man's ; but his head was the head of a bull ; and his teeth were the teeth of a lion, and with them he tore his prey. And when he saw Theseus he roared, and put his head down, and rushed right at him.

But Theseus stept aside nimbly, and as he passed by, cut him in the knee ; and ere he could turn in the narrow path, he followed him, and stabbed him again and again from behind, till the monster fled bellowing wildly ; for he never before had felt a wound. And Theseus followed him at full speed, holding the clue of thread in his left hand.

Then on, through cavern after cavern, under dark ribs of sounding stone, and up rough glens and torrent-beds, among the sunless roots of Ida, and to the edge of the eternal snow, went they, the hunter and the hunted, while the hills bellowed to the monster's bellow.

And at last Theseus came up with him, where he lay panting on a slab among the snow, and caught him by the horns, and forced his head back, and drove the keen sword through his throat.

Then he turned, and went back limping and weary, feeling his way down by the clue of thread, till he came to the mouth of that doleful place ; and saw waiting for him, whom but Ariadne !

And he whispered, " It is done ! " and showed her the sword ; and she laid her finger on her lips, and led him to the prison, and opened the doors, and set all the prisoners free, while the guards lay sleeping heavily ; for she had silenced them with wine.

Then they fled to their ship together, and leapt on board, and hoisted up the sail ; and the night lay dark around them, so that they passed through Minos' ships, and escaped all safe to Naxos ; and there Ariadne became Theseus' wife.

CHARLES KINGSLEY, *The Heroes* (adapted)

THE STORY OF TROY

THE APPLE OF DISCORD

THERE was great rejoicing on Olympus at the wedding-feast of Peleus and the sea-nymph Thetis. Thither went all the Immortals, at the bidding of Zeus, save only Eris, the goddess of Discord, who, since she spoiled all merry-making with her quarrelsome ways, had not been asked by the King of Heaven. She, however, came uninvited, and into the midst of the gods and goddesses, when the mirth was at its height, threw an apple of pure gold, with the inscription " For the Fairest." At once the goddesses began to discuss to whom this gift should go ; one and all laid claim to it, but three persisted in demanding it.

Aphrodite, the goddess of love and beauty, declared that of course the apple was hers, but Hera, the Queen of Heaven, would not allow that any goddess should be considered more beautiful than she, and Pallas Athene, goddess of wisdom, claiming beauty as well as wisdom, would not relinquish her claim.

In this dilemma the gods were asked to give their opinion, but none of them, not even Zeus himself, would dare to give judgment, and it was agreed to leave the decision to Paris, himself the most beautiful of mortal men, and therefore deemed worthy to judge of divine beauty.

J. M. M.

THE JUDGMENT OF PARIS

PARIS was one of the sons born to Priam, King of Troy, and his wife Hecuba ; but at his birth the oracles of the

77

gods had demanded that he should die, foretelling that he would be the death of his kindred and the ruin of his country ; and Priam, his father, sorrowfully handed over the wailing baby to the priest, to be exposed upon Mount Ida. But first he tied an old ring about his neck ; and when Paris was strangely saved from death, he grew up to be the fairest and strongest of all the shepherd youths on Ida.

One day he came by accident to Troy. This stripling from the glens of Mount Ida competed in the games outside the city, and was so successful that the Trojans were jealous of the handsome stranger who carried off the prizes from them. Soon he found himself embroiled with Priam's athletic sons. He was hard beset. The odds were heavy against him ; and like a hunted animal he flung himself before the altar of Apollo for protection.

Cassandra, the priestess of Apollo, had never before seen this young suppliant who was clinging to the altar ; but as she looked on him now there came upon her a revelation of his identity. She knew of the old ring which had been placed about her baby brother's neck when he was exposed to death upon the mountain ; and, taking Paris by the hand, she touched the chain he wore and slowly drew to light the talisman.

> This sign Cassandra showed to Priam straight.
> The king waxed pale and asked what this might be ?
> And she made answer, " Sir, and King, thy fate
> That comes on all men born hath come on thee ;
> This shepherd is thine own child verily." [1]

But the old king would not be warned against his fate. He welcomed his boy as one returned from death. A great festival was made in his honour ; and joy and merriment filled the city. All the warning oracles which had spoken

[1] From Andrew Lang's *Helen of Troy*.

at the birth of Paris were forgotten. Nothing but thanksgiving was heard for the restoration of the fair young prince. Thenceforward the poor shepherd was the best beloved of all the princes. Life went gaily ; and for a while he was utterly content. But he had left behind, amidst the groves of Mount Ida, a sweet wood-nymph who loved him well, Oenone. And when, after a time, he began to tire of life in the palace, he remembered her and thought longingly of the freshness and beauty of the mountain. So one day in summer he went to seek Oenone. All day long he searched the forest, but could not find her ; and coming tired at evening to a fragrant glade, he fell asleep. When he awoke night was hushed all around, and stars peeped through the slender branches overhead. It was midnight and there was no moon ; but it was not dark. The glade was filled with a soft radiance such as he had never seen before, and when he raised his wondering eyes he saw the majestical figures of goddesses shining upon him : Hera, Queen of Olympus, Athene, the wise maid of Zeus, and Aphrodite, the laughing goddess of love. Sweetly they smiled on him ; and as he stood in wondering awe, the deep, rich tones of Hera sank upon his spirit, promising him greatness and power, and the lordship over many lands. Then Athene, resting her starlike gaze upon him, promised him wisdom and courage, and Aphrodite, with a little mocking laugh at power and at wisdom, promised him the fairest woman in the world. Only, and this was to be the price of the gift, he was to be the arbiter between them : he was to declare which was most beautiful.

There was only one answer possible to Paris. Ambition had no lure for him. Why fight and strive and spend the happy days in effort merely to be called great ? And wisdom had no appeal for him either ; she seemed austere and cold. What had she to do with the joy and grace and sweetness that his soul loved ? To the sublimity of Hera he bent in awe. The shining purity of Athene smote his glance to the earth. But the voice of Aphrodite wooed him, and her winsome smile set him trembling with delight. He reached out to her the golden prize of beauty.

So Paris was to gain the fairest woman in the world. It seemed an honest promise, full of the happiest portent ; and the young Prince soon set out upon his search for a bride over the western seas. But Aphrodite was no better than a cheat, and had invoked on Paris, though he did not know it then, the curse of guilty love. For the exquisite child who was to be the world's queen of beauty had grown up in the home of Tyndareus, King of Sparta ; and even while the goddess gave her word to Paris was happily married to Menelaus there. To her and to her husband Paris came in his wanderings, led unwittingly by the laughter-loving goddess, and clothed by her in beauty like a god. They feasted him and did him honour ; and sitting at the banquet which they made to him he told the strange tale of his life and his quest.

Helen listened to his story with a sudden prescience of what was to come ; and rising softly, left the banqueting hall and went away to implore the goddess to avert the doom. But she was no match for Aphrodite. Anger and entreaty could not move the wanton Olympian, but she would grant one boon—Helen should be oblivious of all her past. Under the spell, the love of husband and child faded out ; and even the memory of them vanished when on that spring morning in the garden of the palace, Paris met her beside the stream, " 'twixt the lily and the rose."

Together they fled in the dewy morning, Paris urging his horses with guilty haste to the ships. And there, with Menelaus thundering along after them, they set sail for Troy, fulfilling the old prophecy, and lighting a brand by their deed which should burn the sacred city to the ground. For Tyndareus, when he chose a husband for Helen amongst her many suitors, had won a promise that they would all defend the one who gained her. Agamemnon, brother to Menelaus, and the great overlord of the Hellenic princes, now summoned the allies to avenge his brother, and for ten years they toiled at fitting out a fleet. Then they " launched a thousand ships," and sailed to punish Troy for the sin of Paris.

Meanwhile Helen had wakened sadly from the spell of Aphrodite. Little by little memory of her home came back, and with it came remorse. The Trojans, who at first had welcomed her as a goddess, soon began to look askance at her when rumours came of the great siege that was preparing. Mothers and wives of the Trojan princes held aloof ; and soon the only friends left to her were the kind old King and Hector, the noble defender of the city. But there was worse behind. Little by little the truth dawned that Paris, for whom she had lost so much, and who had seemed so godlike in his strength and beauty, was very poor humanity indeed. The story of Oenone was told to her ; and that showed him unfaithful. And when the leaguer actually lay beneath the walls she soon found that Paris was a coward too.

For nearly ten years the cruel siege wasted Troy. The armies, reduced by death and pestilence and famine, were beginning to murmur against the worthless cause of all their misery ; and Paris, for very shame, could no longer shelter himself within the city. At this eleventh hour he issued out to meet Menelaus in single combat. Helen was sitting in her inner hall, weaving a purple web and embroidering upon it the battle scenes which ebbed and flowed around the walls. Time and sorrow had only given her beauty an added charm. She was still young, fresh, and exquisitely fair, as on that spring morning in

F

Lacedaemon when Aphrodite graced her for the meeting with Paris. To her, as her sweet face bent over the web, the goddess Iris brought news of the impending combat : " They that erst waged fearful war upon each other in the plain, eager for deadly battle, now sit in silence, and the battle is stayed, and they lean upon their shields, and the tall spears are planted by their sides. But Paris and Menelaus, dear to Ares, will fight with their tall spears for thee ; and thou wilt be declared the dear wife of him that conquereth."

M. C. STURGEON, *Women of the Classics* (adapted)

DUEL BETWEEN PARIS AND MENELAUS

WHEN Paris saw Menelaus coming his guilty heart quailed within him, and he shrank back among the ranks of his comrades, like one who has trodden on a snake while walking in a mountain glen.

" Now curse on thy fair, false face ! " cried Hector to his cowardly brother, " thou carpet-knight, thou foul deceiver ! Better for thee to have died childless and unwed than thus to bring shame on thy father and all thy kinsfolk and people. Thou art a fit foe for women, whom thou beguilest with witchcraft of thy wit, and wicked gifts ; but all thy gifts—thy curling locks, thy smooth, white brow, thy sweet voice, and cunning minstrelsy— avail thee naught when thou lookest upon the face of a man. Verily the Trojans are as dastardly as thyself, or long ere this thou wouldst have put on a doublet of stone for all the ills that thou hast wrought."

" I have deserved thy rebuke," answered Paris. " Keen as the blade of an axe, which bites deep into the heart of an oak, when wielded by a sinewy arm, so is the keenness of thy spirit, and thou knowest not fear. Nevertheless, mock me not for the lovely gifts of Aphrodite, for the gifts of heaven are not to be despised. And if thou desirest me to take up this quarrel with Menelaus thou hast thy wish. I will fight against him hand to hand, and he who is victor shall be lord of Helen and all her possessions. So shall the long strife have an end, and peace shall dwell again within our borders."

When Hector heard his brother's bold words he was glad, and gave the word to make the Trojans sit down in their ranks. At first the Greeks did not understand what was happening, and pressed onward to the attack with a shower of stones and arrows; but Agamemnon soon perceived that Hector had something to propose, and gave the signal for a general halt.

Then Hector, standing midway between the two armies, made known the offer of Paris, and asked for an armistice, that the two champions might try the issue between them. All eyes were now turned on Menelaus, who responded boldly to the challenge. " I am well content," said he, " that this quarrel should be decided by the hands of us twain ; for it grieves my heart that so many should suffer for the sake of my private wrong. Let two lambs be brought—a white ram as an offering to the sun, and a black ram as an offering to the earth ; and go some of you to fetch Priam, that he may preside at the treaty. His sons we may not trust, for they are hot-blooded and faithless ; but an old man's head is cool, and his eye looks before and after."

Right pleased were both Greeks and Trojans when the order was sent round to dismount from their cars and pile their arms ; for they thought that the end of their bitter feud was near. Two heralds were dispatched to bring down Priam from the city, and Agamemnon sent another for a victim to be sacrificed on behalf of the Greeks.

Priam set out at once, taking with him the victims required for the sacrifice. When he came to the open

space between the two armies he found all things ready
for a solemn rite. The chiefs stood waiting in a circle,
and in their midst was Agamemnon, who acted as priest.
The heralds mingled two portions of pure wine in a bowl,
and poured water over the hands of the chieftains. Then
Agamemnon drew a sharp knife, which hung at his girdle
by his ponderous sword, and cutting off a few hairs from
the foreheads of the victims, gave them to the heralds to
distribute among the princes. When this was done,
amidst a general hush he uttered this solemn prayer :
" Father Zeus, Lord of Ida, most glorious, most mighty,
ye rivers, and thou earth, and ye dread powers beneath,
who take vengeance after death on all those who swear a
false oath, be ye all the witnesses and guardians of our
treaty. If Paris slays Menelaus he shall keep Helen for
his wife, with all her goods ; but should Paris fall Helen
shall go back to Menelaus, her lawful lord. Let the war
be decided by the issue of this combat, and Heaven defend
the right ! " Therewith he cut the throats of the victims,
and laid their quivering bodies on the ground. Then the
drink-offering was poured, with this awful imprecation on
those who should break the treaty : " If any man violate
our sworn oath, may his brains be poured out even as
this wine, and may his wife and children be sold into
bondage."

Priam now took his departure from the field, for he
could not bear to see his son in deadly combat with
Menelaus. When he was gone, Hector and Odysseus
measured out the ground for the duel, and shook the
lots in a helmet, to see who should be the first to cast his
spear ; and the lot fell on Paris. Meanwhile Paris was
putting on his armour ; for he had come lightly equipped
as an archer into the field.

The two rivals took their stand on either side, clad
in their brazen harness, and armed with sword and spear.

And first Paris cast his spear, which struck upon the shield of Menelaus and did him no harm. Then Menelaus lifted up his spear, and murmured a prayer to Zeus : " Grant me, O King, to take vengeance on him who brought dishonour on my home, where he dwelt as my honoured guest." As he spoke, he flung his good ashen spear, which clove its way through the shield of Paris, and tore his tunic close to his side ; but Paris swerved aside and escaped a wound. Before he could recover himself Menelaus was upon him, sword in hand, and struck him with all his force upon the helmet ; but once more fortune favoured the Trojan, for the blade was shivered on the ridge of the helmet, and Menelaus grasped a useless hilt. " Curse on thee, treacherous steel ! " cried he, and seizing Paris by the helmet, began to drag him towards the ranks of the Greeks. This time he would have succeeded, and taken his enemy captive, had not the strap which held the helmet given way under the strain, so that the brazen headpiece came away empty in his hand.

Menelaus flung the helmet towards his friends, and picking up his spear turned again upon his cowardly foe, with purpose to slay him. But Paris was nowhere to be seen : an invisible hand had caught him up, and carried him away from the righteous hand of the avenger. For Aphrodite, the soft goddess of love, had been hovering near to protect her favourite. She it was who had caused the helmet strap to break, and now she saved him a second time, and bore him swiftly to his house in Troy. There he was presently visited by the lovely Helen, who, though she scorned him in her heart, was drawn thither by a fatal spell which she could not resist ; and in the sunshine of her smiles he soon forgot dishonour and defeat.

All this time Menelaus was raging about the field like a tiger robbed of his prey, and calling upon the Trojans

to surrender the recreant to his vengeance ; and they
would gladly have done so, if they had known where to
find him, for they hated him worse than death.

H. L. HAVELL, *Stories from the Iliad*

THE DEATH OF HECTOR

[IN the ninth year of the war a quarrel arose between
Agamemnon and Achilles over the spoil of a captured
town.   In wrath at the insult done to him Achilles vowed
to take no further part in the fighting until his wrong had
been redressed, but while he " sulked in his tent " his
dear friend Patroclus was slain by Hector.   This event
brought the Greek hero forth again, raging in grief and
anger.   Furnished with new armour which his goddess
mother had obtained from Hephaistos, he fell upon the
Trojans like a destroying flame and drove them within
the gates with terrible slaughter.   Hector alone remained
outside the Skaian gates.]

Achilles was now close at hand, with the mighty Pelian
ash swaying on his right shoulder, and his armour blazing
like the light of the rising sun.   When Hector saw him
advancing, like an incarnate spirit of vengeance, all his
heroic resolves forsook him, and seized with sudden
terror he turned and fled.   And as a falcon swoops down
on a hare, and pounces, and pounces again, as his victim
leaps and doubles, to escape from the fatal clutch, so
Achilles darted after Hector, following all the turns and
windings of his flight.   Past a low hill they went, whence
the Trojan scout had espied the advance of the Greeks
not many days before, and past the wild fig-tree, following
a beaten road, which led to two fair springs, the double
source of eddying Scamander.   One of the springs is of
hot water, and a cloud of steam hangs over it, like the
smoke of a burning fire ; but the other is cold as ice.

Here were broad washing-pits, lined with stone, in which the wives and daughters were wont to tread the clothes, in the old peaceful days, before ever the Greeks had landed on the shores of Troy. Leaving these behind them, they sped on, and still on, pursuer and pursued. Noble was the quarry, but the hunter was nobler far, and never before had he run in so keen a chase. Like mettled steeds, which strive for the mastery, where the prize is a vessel of gold or of silver, they flew ; but here they were running for a far higher stake, even the very life of Troy's bravest son.

Three times they compassed the whole circuit of the walls, and again and again Hector tried to draw his pursuer within range of the spears of the Trojans who lined the battlements ; but each time his effort was defeated by Achilles, who barred his way to the city, and drove him back into the open plain.

As one who pursues his enemy in a dream, and cannot catch him, though he seems ever within reach, so was Achilles ever baffled, when he strove to overtake Hector, and Hector, when he strove to escape. All the Greeks stood near in their ranks, watching the chase—and many a time a spear was levelled at Hector, to strike him down ; but Achilles beckoned with his hand, and forbade his comrades to come between him and his victim.

For the fourth time they came to the place of the washing-pits, and here by mutual consent they paused to draw breath ; for both were sore spent with running, and could not go a step farther. As Achilles stood panting, and leaning on his spear, Athene drew near to him, unseen of all the rest, and said : " He cannot escape us now, though Apollo should grovel in the dust at the feet of Zeus, begging for his life. Remain awhile and recover thy strength, and I will go and persuade him to fight thee face to face."

About an arrow's flight distant, Hector had come to

a standstill, and drooped heavily, resting his hands on his knees, half strangled by his efforts to breathe. Suddenly, to his amazement, he saw Deiphobus, his brother, standing by his side, and heard the familiar tones of his voice. " Dear brother," said Deiphobus, " thou art hard beset, and driven to bay by this fierce son of Peleus. But lo ! I am here to aid thee, and I will not fail thee in this strait."

" Deiphobus," answered Hector, " thou wert ever dearest to me of all the sons whom Hecuba bore to Priam : but now thou art dear and honoured too, since alone of all my nation thou hast dared to leave the shelter of the walls."

" Ay," answered the pretended Deiphobus, " my mother and my father, and all my friends, strove to hold me back ; but my heart yearned towards thee in thy mortal need. But come with me, and together we will try the fortune of war. Go thou first, and I will follow."

Hector accordingly advanced to meet Achilles, who was already moving towards him. " I will fly thee no more," he said, when they were within a spear's cast of each other, " I will either slay thee, or be slain. But let us first make a covenant, and call the gods to witness it ; swear thou that, if I fall, thou wilt restore my body and my armour to the Trojans—and I will swear to do the like by thee."

" Talk not to me of covenants, thou villain ! " answered Achilles fiercely. " As there is no treaty possible between lions and men, no concord between wolves and lambs, but only fear and hatred, so is there hate unending between me and thee, which naught but death may cancel or abate. Summon up all thy manhood, and prepare to pay the price of my comrades whom thou hast slain."

This said he poised and flung his spear ; but Hector

stooped low, and the spear flew over his head, and sank deep into the earth. Unobserved by Hector, Athene drew it out, and gave it back to Achilles. " Take now my spear ! " shouted the Trojan, " take it to thy heart, thou braggart, that thinkest to dismay me with boastful words ! " The weapon flew straight to its mark, and, striking the centre of Achilles' shield, rebounded to a distance, and fell rattling on the ground. Then Hector called anxiously to Deiphobus, bidding him bring another lance. But no answer came, for the real Deiphobus was safe behind the walls, and he who had appeared to Hector was a false Deiphobus, concealing the person of Athene.

" Alas ! I have been deceived," said Hector. " My last bolt is shot, and my fate summons me to death. Let me not die inglorious and without a struggle, but in such wise that I shall be named with honour by generations yet unborn."

Then, drawing his sword, he rushed upon Achilles, who came on slowly, towering above the rampart of his shield, nodding his golden plumes and brandishing high his spear, whose point twinkled and flashed like the light of the evening star. Scanning every joint in Hector's armour, at last Achilles spied a point, between the shoulder-blade and the neck, which was undefended ; and at this mark he hurled his spear with all his force and pierced him through the neck. But the passage of his voice was left untouched, so that he was able to speak.

" Thou hast paid thy debt to Patroclus," said Achilles, standing over his fallen enemy, " and now thou shalt pay the usury. Dogs and vultures shall give thee burial, but he shall lie in an honoured tomb."

" By thy life," answered Hector faintly, " by thy father's name, I implore thee, give not my body to be devoured by dogs, but restore it to my friends, who will pay thee a heavy ransom, that I may receive my due in death."

"Thou dog!" replied Achilles, with a furious look, "talk not of thy dues, nor name my father to me! Would that I could find it in my heart to carve and devour thy flesh, as surely as thou shalt not escape the hounds and vultures, no, not if Priam were to offer thy weight in gold, after what thou hast done unto me and mine."

"I knew that I should not persuade thee," said Hector, with his dying breath. "Thou hast a heart of iron. But vengeance shall reach thee in the day when Apollo and Paris shall subdue thee at the gates of Troy."

As he uttered this prophecy a shudder ran through his limbs, and the gallant spirit fled to the land of shadows.

"Die!" said Achilles, as Hector uttered his last sigh. "As for me, I am prepared to meet my fate whensoever Heaven wills its accomplishment."

Then he drew out his spear, and laying it aside, began to strip off the armour which Hector had taken from Patroclus. And the Greeks came crowding round, to gaze on the beauty and stature of Hector, and stab the helpless body with their spears. Far other had he seemed to them when he came with fire and sword to burn their ships, and fill their camp with slaughter!

When Achilles had done stripping the corpse, he stood up and spoke thus to the assembled host:

"Princes and counsellors of the Greeks, now that the gods have granted us to slay this mighty champion, who hath done us more harm than all the rest together, shall we not advance in full force against the city, and end the war at one bold stroke? But alas! what am I saying? We have another and a sadder duty to perform. Patroclus lies among the ships, unburied, unwept, and shall I forget him in this hour of triumph? No; not in the hour of death, not in the grave itself, which brings, they say, oblivion to all, shall my love for him grow cold. Therefore follow me, sirs, to the ships, and raise the song of victory. We have gained great glory, we have slain Troy's chief defender, to whom all the Trojans prayed as to a god."

Then, in fulfilment of his horrible menaces, he prepared to take hideous vengeance on his slaughtered enemy. Stooping down he pierced the dead man's feet from heel to ankle, and passed a leathern thong through the holes ; then he made fast the thong behind the chariot, and, taking up the armour, he sprang into the driver's place, and lashed his horses to a gallop. So amid a swirling cloud of dust the fallen hero was dragged along, with his dark locks streaming, and that comely head marred and defiled ; and Zeus delivered him to injury and outrage at the hands of his enemies in his own native land.

H. L. HAVELL, *Stories from the Iliad*

THE DEATH OF PARIS

OENONE sat within the cave from out
Whose ivy-matted mouth she used to gaze
Down at the Troad. . . .
    Anon from out the long ravine below,
She heard a wailing cry, that seem'd at first
Thin as the batlike shrillings of the Dead
When driven to Hades, but, in coming near,
Across the downward thunder of the brook
Sounded " Oenone " ; and on a sudden he,
Paris, no longer beauteous as a God,
Struck by a poison'd arrow in the fight,
Lame, crooked, reeling, livid, thro' the mist
Rose, like the wraith of his dead self, and moan't
" Oenone, *my* Oenone, while we dwelt

Together in this valley—happy then—
Too happy had I died within thine arms,
Before the feud of Gods had marr'd our peace,
And sunder'd each from each. I am dying now
Pierced by a poison'd dart. Save me. Thou knowest,
Taught by some God, whatever herb or balm
May clear the blood from poison, and thy fame
Is blown thro' all the Troad, and to thee
The shepherd brings his adder-bitten lamb,
The wounded warrior climbs from Troy to thee.
My life and death are in thy hand. The Gods
Avenge on stony hearts a fruitless prayer
For pity. Let me owe my life to thee.
I wrought thee bitter wrong, but thou forgive,
Forget it. Man is but the slave of Fate.
Oenone, by thy love which once was mine,
Help, heal me. I am poison'd to the heart."

[Refusing to help, Oenone upbraided him with bitter
words for his cruel desertion of her.]

He groan'd, he turn'd, and in the mist at once
Became a shadow, sank and disappear'd,
But, ere the mountain rolls into the plain,
Fell headlong dead ; and of the shepherds one
Their oldest, and the same who first had found
Paris, a naked babe, among the woods
Of Ida, following lighted on him there,
And shouted, and the shepherds heard and came.
   One raised the Prince, one sleek'd the squalid hair,
One kiss'd his hand, another closed his eyes,
And then, remembering the gay playmate rear'd
Among them, and forgetful of the man,
Whose crime had half unpeopled Ilion, these
All that day long labour'd, hewing the pines,
And built their shepherd-prince a funeral pile ;

And, while the star of eve was drawing light
From the dead sun, kindled the pyre, and all
Stood round it, hush'd, or calling on his name.

LORD TENNYSON, *The Death of Oenone*

THE FALL OF TROY

IT is the hour of early dawn, and the drowsy sentinels are
nodding at their posts on Priam's royal citadel. A great
stillness lies on all the city of Troy, and many a weary
soul is enjoying a brief respite from the toil and agony
of the ten years' siege. Then suddenly a voice is heard,
breaking the deathlike silence : " Awake, Trojans,
awake ! The Greeks have fled ; their camp is deserted ;
Troy is saved ! " Again and again the mysterious voice
is heard, starting the echoes in the empty streets ; and
soon a low murmur arises in a thousand dwellings, like
the first faint hum of an awakening hive. There is a
crash of opening doors, and just as the first rays of the
sun are reddening the battlements of Pergamus, a vast
multitude is seen pouring through the streets, pressing
with tumult and uproar towards the Skaian Gate. Through
the open portals it rushes, past the tomb of Ilus, across the
plain, and down to the sea.

Yes, the voice has spoken truly : the Greeks have gone,
and there lies their camp, dismantled and deserted. The
crowd disperses, and spreads along the whole shore, and
here and there a little group is seen gathered round some
scarred warrior as he points out each memorable spot.
" See, here stood the tent of Achilles ; here lay Odysseus,
with the men of Ithaca ; here Hector broke the rampart,
and carried fire and slaughter into the very heart of the
camp." But before long all are hurrying in one direction,
attracted by a strange cry which runs from lip to lip :
" The Wooden Horse ! " Let us follow the footsteps of

that tall warrior who is leading a little child by the hand, and we shall learn the meaning of that repeated cry.

In an open space, not far from the shore, towers a huge wooden fabric, shaped like a horse, with stout pillars of oak for legs. A great crowd, whose numbers are swelling every moment, is gathered round the monster, and a clamour of voices is heard, questioning, explaining, and disputing. " It is a gift of the gods," cries one ; " we must guard it and keep it in the citadel of Troy." Perhaps he was a traitor, perhaps only an unconscious instrument of Heaven's will. Soon the multitude is divided into two parties : one is for harbouring the gift of the Greeks in the city ; the other insists that it should be hacked to pieces, and burnt with fire.

While they are debating thus, a man of tall stature and majestic mien breaks through the throng, and takes his stand before the horse. It is Laocoön, one of the chief men of Troy. " Madmen ! " he cries in loud and excited tones, " do ye indeed believe that the enemy has gone ? Do ye think that they have left this thing out of loving-kindness to us ? Look at that mountain of timber : would ye know what it is ?—a place of ambush or an engine of destruction ; or whatever be its purpose, be assured that it bodes no good to us. A boon to Troy !—and from the Greeks ! Have ye never heard their own proverb, ' The gift of a foe shall work thee woe ' ? " With that he poised a weighty spear, and hurled it with all his force against the timber ribs of the beast. Deep into its side pierced the iron point, and the shaft of ash stood quivering ; and from the hollow vault within came a sound like a groan.

Some praised the deed of Laocoön and some stood aghast at his impiety ; but presently a bustle was heard on the outskirts of the crowd, and a new arrival changed the current of their thoughts. To the place where Priam, the aged King of Troy, stood anxiously consulting with his elders, a little troop of shepherds came hurrying, dragging with them a prisoner, whose arms were rudely pinioned with a cord. His features and dress proclaimed him to be a Greek; and while a hundred hands were raised to strike him down, and a hundred voices mocked his struggles, he rolled his eyes wildly round that circle of scornful faces, and uttered this despairing cry : " Lost, lost—all lost ! No place for me left on land or sea ! In Greece I am an outlaw, and the Trojans have but one thought—that I am a Greek."

Struck by his words and gestures Priam restrains the violence of the people, and gives orders to unbind the captive's arms. " Now speak," he commands, " if thou hast aught to tell which may profit us and thee." Thus encouraged, the prisoner explains that his name is Sinon, and that he is flying from the vengeance of Odysseus, who sought his death because he had denounced the murder of Palamedes, his friend and benefactor, in which the crafty Ithacan had borne the chief part. When the Greeks, who had abandoned the siege of Troy, and resolved to return to Greece, were detained by contrary winds, Calchas, the chief prophet of the army, proclaimed the necessity of appeasing the hostile powers of the air by the sacrifice of a human victim. Odysseus saw his opportunity, and secretly instigated Calchas to name Sinon as the man destined to suffer for the sins of the people. This was welcome news to the Greeks ; for every one had been quaking with fear lest he himself should be singled out for the altar and the knife. Sinon was seized, and kept in close custody ; but on the eve of the fatal day he contrived to break his bonds, and lay hiding in a swamp, until he fell into the hands of the Trojan shepherds.

Such is the well-imagined tale, broken with sobs and sighs, which the arch-dissembler pours into the ears of his captors. He finds ready credence ; Priam himself takes him by the hand, with assurance of pity and protection. "Forget that thou art a Greek," he says; "henceforth thou shalt be one of us. And now tell me truly, to what end was this wooden monster built? Is it an offering to the gods or is it an engine of war?" Then Sinon, whose confidence is fully restored, lifts up his hands to Heaven, and cries: "By yonder everlasting fires, and by the sacred altar flame, and by the dear life which ye have given back to me, I swear that I will renounce my fealty to the Greeks and tell thee all the truth. This horse is an offering of atonement to the offended majesty of Pallas Athene, whose sore anger was kindled against the Greeks since the day when Odysseus and Diomede broke into the citadel of Troy and defiled her temple with blood. From that hour all their hopes were broken, and every attack on your city was foiled. At last Calchas bade them return to Greece, and win back the favour of Pallas by solemn sacrifice and prayer in her native seat. They are now in full sail for Mycenae, and when all rites are paid they will come back and renew the war. This wooden horse is a peace-offering to Pallas, to replace the image which Diomede and Odysseus profaned; and it was made of gigantic size to prevent it from being carried into your city, for once it finds shelter in the walls of Troy, Pallas Athene will be pledged to your defence, and all the hosts of Greece will dash themselves against your walls in vain."

Sinon has played his part well; his tragic story, told with well-feigned passion, has opened the hearts of the Trojans towards him and prepared their minds to receive all his glozing lies as Heaven's own truth. If any shadow of doubt remained it was removed by the terrible fate which overtook Laocoön on the same day. Being chosen by lot as priest of Poseidon, he was sacrificing a bull at the altar on the beach; and his two sons were with him.

to aid him in his office. Just as his hand was raised to
strike the victim a strange sound fell upon his ears, as of
some great vessel rushing rapidly over the calm waters,
and, glancing seaward, he saw two monster serpents
speeding towards the shore, with towering crests, like the
prow of some huge galley. In a moment they had reached
the land, and, rolling their enormous coils along the
rattling pebbles, made straight for the spot where Laocoön's
two sons stood, transfixed with terror. Knife in hand, he
rushed to defend them ; but already the serpents had
flung their folds around the tender limbs of the lads, and
now father and sons are wrapped in the same hideous
embrace. In vain the mighty man wrestles and heaves
at those knotted coils which close tighter and tighter
round him ; his shrieks of agony sink into stifled moans ;
there is a horrible cracking sound ; then all is still, and
three shattered corpses lie crushed together on the field.

At this plain evidence of Heaven's will conviction is
borne home to every heart. " He has suffered for his
sin," cry the people with one voice, " because he lifted
his hand against the sacred image of the gods. Quick !
let us lodge the horse in our citadel, and pray that his
sin be not visited on us and on our children." Then
not a hand remains idle in all the town ; some bring
ropes and rollers and wheels ; some make a breach in
the walls, for the gates are too narrow to give passage to
that enormous bulk. A thousand sturdy warriors are
harnessed to the unwieldy machine, and the strange procession begins, while little children strew the way with
flowers, and go before with dance and song.

It is done ; the fatal steed, with its burden of armed
warriors, is stabled in the centre of the city ; and all the
hosts of Troy give themselves up to a joyful revel, with
hymns of praise and thankfulness to Heaven. Then,
heavy with wine and weary with their labours, they sink

a

into a dreamless sleep, and night descends upon the devoted town

Meanwhile the Grecian fleet has been lying at anchor off Tenedos, just out of sight of the walls of Troy. The hour has come, every man is at his post, and at a given signal the whole armada is sweeping through the darkness towards the coast of Asia. In Troy Sinon is on the alert, and at the first distant sound of trampling feet he steals swiftly to the place where the wooden horse is stationed, and releases his comrades from their dark prison. They are nine in number, and among them are Menelaus, the brother of Agamemnon, Neoptolemus, son of Achilles, and the crafty Odysseus. Without a word they rush through the dark and deserted streets ; the warders are cut down, the gates are flung open, and before any alarm can be given the whole host of Greece is pouring through the gates and over the unguarded breach.

In a secluded part of the city, sheltered from the public thoroughfare by a dense growth of trees, stands the house of Anchises, an aged prince of Troy, honoured in his youth by the love of Aphrodite. The fruit of that union was Aeneas, who since Hector's death has been the chief champion of Troy against the Greeks ; and here he lives with his father Anchises, now old and blind, his wife Creüsa, and his little son Iulus. Aeneas had retired at an early hour, worn out by the toils and revels of that eventful day ; but in the first sweet sleep of night his repose was disturbed by a strange vision : before him stood the form of Hector, not as he appeared in his hour of pride, when he came back clothed in the armour of Achilles, but such as he was after he had been slain and dragged behind the car of his slayer, his hair and beard clotted with gore and defiled with dust, and his feet pierced for the thongs. Aeneas was moved to tears by the sight of those loved features, now so foully marred, and

strove to speak ; but the spectre motioned him to be
silent, and thus addressed him in a hollow and mournful
voice : " Fly, goddess-born ! The foe is within the walls,
and Troy is already in flames ; if mortal hand could have
saved her, that task would have been mine. For thee a
happier destiny is in store, and thou shalt found a new
Troy in lands beyond the sea." Then he brought the
sacred image of Hestia from the shrine, placed it in the
hands of Aeneas, and vanished from his sight.

Hardly had the ghostly voice died away when other
and far more dreadful sounds roused Aeneas from his
fevered sleep, and, springing from his couch, he clothed
himself hastily, and ascended to the flat roof of the
palace. As he emerged into the open air a roar like a
hundred winter torrents smote upon his ear ; from every
part of the city came cries of despair and yells of triumph,
and flames were beginning to break out in more than one
quarter. Realizing at once that Troy had been betrayed,
Aeneas descended the narrow stairway, flung himself into
his armour, and, seizing spear and shield, rushed out to
take his part in the defence. Soon he was joined by a
little band of Trojans as desperate as himself, and together
they plunged into the thickest of the fight, with but one
thought and one hope—to slay and be slain.

What words can describe the carnage of that night or
paint the scene of Troy's last agony ? An ancient city is
falling after a thousand years of empire ; her streets are
strewn with dead and dying, her temple gates are splashed
with blood ; nor is it only the Trojans who pay the dreadful debt of war—victor and vanquished are stretched side
by side, sleeping their iron sleep together, and above them
the demon of battle still rages on. . . .

Night is descending on the burning town, and Aeneas,
who has played a hero's part in all these scenes of horror,
finds himself standing in a deserted spot, unwounded, and

alone. So sudden has been the revulsion from that brief
hour of peace and happiness, when it seemed that their
ten years' struggle was at last crowned with triumph,
that he feels like a man who has awakened from a hideous
dream, and pauses, in this moment of respite, to collect
his thoughts. His mind goes back to his father's house,
where he left Anchises, and Creüsa and her child, when
he rushed forth, bent on death, in the early morning.
The debt to king and country has been paid ; he will
strive no longer against irresistible fate, but will go and
see how his own dear ones have fared, and save them,
if it is not too late. With this resolve he turns his steps
homeward, avoiding the frequented streets, now thronged
by the victorious soldiers of Agamemnon ; and arriving
home finds Anchises, Creüsa, and Iulus still safe and sound.

But when Aeneas sought to take his father in his arms,
and bear him away from the town, the old man stub-
bornly refused to leave his home. " 'Tis for you," he
cried, " who are still in the flush and glow of youth—
'tis for you to think of flight. As for me, I am a useless
burden, a shattered and sightless trunk, and I am resolved
to fall with my city's fall. Is it not enough that I have
once seen Troy in ruins and once survived her over-
throw ? I am already dead : lay me out, as for burial, and
depart." In vain his son and his daughter and his grand-
son besieged him with entreaty ; like a man stunned with
sorrow he lay with his face to the wall, waiting for death.

Maddened by this unlooked-for obstacle Aeneas
snatched up his sword, and was preparing to seek out the
thickest of the fight, and perish sword in hand, when
Creüsa flung herself in his path, implored him to remain,
and not abandon her and her child to lawless outrage. By
her side the child Iulus was kneeling, fixing his eyes with
mute appeal on his father's face. While Aeneas stood
irresolute there befell a wondrous thing. On the head of

Iulus, as he stood between his sorrowing parents, there shot up a sudden point of fire : it blazed and shone, and spread among his clustering curls, and played with innocuous touch round the temples of the child. Aeneas and his wife raised a cry of alarm, and sought to quench the blazing hair ; but Anchises, who had heard their cries, knew better how to interpret the meaning of that hallowed flame. New life seemed to enter his stiffened limbs ; he rose from his couch, lifted up his hands to Heaven, and prayed for a sign to confirm this omen. Hardly had his words been uttered when a loud crash of thunder shook the house, and a flaming meteor shot across the sky, and plunged into the woods of Ida, leaving a luminous track. At this plain answer to his prayer Anchises turned to his son, and said : " It is enough ; Heaven hath declared its will, and I resist no longer. Take me, my son, and carry me whither thou wilt."

Overjoyed at these words of his father Aeneas instantly prepared for flight ; and at this very moment a huge column of fire was seen sweeping towards the house, and a hot blast, as from a furnace, struck upon his face. Hastily summoning his servants, and dismissing them by different routes to a place of meeting outside the town, he robed himself in a lion's hide, and bowed his neck to receive that sacred burden. Anchises took in his hands the images of their household gods, and, borne on his son's broad shoulders, crossed for the last time the threshold of his house ; Iulus took his father's hand, and Creüsa followed at some distance behind. Clinging close to the shadows they went slowly forward ; and now for the first time in his life Aeneas learnt the meaning of fear, and he who had braved all the embattled hosts of Greece started at every sound and trembled at every passing breath of wind. For love makes the heart timid, and three precious lives were now in his charge.

At length they reached the appointed place, a ruined temple of Demeter outside the town, and breathed more freely as they paused to rest beneath the boughs of an ancient cypress-tree. But what was the horror of Aeneas when he called his wife by name and received no answer! She must have missed her way in the darkness, and was nowhere to be seen. Pierced with grief at this sore mischance Aeneas prepared to retrace his steps back to the city. But some time was lost while he sought a secure retreat for his father and child in a deep valley among the wooded spurs of Ida. This duty performed he commended his dear ones to some of his comrades, who had escaped to the same place of refuge, and hurried, unarmed as he was, back to the town.

Cautiously retracing his footsteps, and peering round him for any trace of the lost one, he returns first to his own home, thinking that perhaps she has found her way back thither. Vain hope! As he draws near a great flame leaps up from the roof, and he sees the Greeks hurrying from the burning house laden with spoil. Then onward to the palace of Priam, where all resistance has ceased, and the spoiler's hand is busiest; in the porch stand Phoenix and Odysseus, keeping watch over a vast pile of booty torn from the burning shrines—the rich tables where the gods were wont to sit at meat, bowls of solid gold, and embroidered raiment. Hard by is a piteous band of captive women and children. But nowhere does he see a trace of the lost Creüsa. Frantic with anxiety he flings all caution away, and flies like a madman from street to street, shouting aloud her name, and startling the echoes with his cries. In the midst of his loudest and wildest appeal he halts, arrested by a sudden fear; the air seems to grow cold around him, and his mortal flesh shudders and shrinks, as if conscious of an unseen presence; then out of the ebon darkness a dim white radiance appears, growing slowly into definite shape, and assuming the form and countenance of the vanished Creüsa, but taller in stature, and more majestic in mien, and clothed with an awful beauty which she had never worn before. Gazing on him with calm, sad eyes she spoke these words, softly and sweetly, shedding peace upon his soul : " What avails this stormy passion of sorrow, dear lord of my heart ? It was not the will of him who sits enthroned in heaven's high citadel that I should follow thee hence and share thy long wanderings and distant exile. Far away in the West lies thy goal, and there thou shalt find a new kingdom and a royal bride. Weep not for me, nor fear that I, a daughter of Dardanus and the consort of Aeneas, shall ever brook the lot of servitude in the halls of a proud Grecian dame. My fate detains me here, a hand-maid in the train of Cybele, the mighty mother of the gods. Farewell, and remember that thou owest more than a father's love to Iulus, the dear pledge of our wedded joy." Aeneas listened weeping, and when she had finished opened his lips to reply, and stretched out his arms to clasp the form of his beloved ; but ere he had uttered a word the vision was gone, and his arms closed on the empty air.

Sorrowful, but no longer desperate, he found his way back to the spot where he had left his father and child. As he drew near the murmur of a great multitude greeted his wondering ears ; for all who had escaped from the sack of the city had flocked hither with their wives and children to share the fortunes of their banished prince. Behind them all the sky was red with the flames of their desolated homes ; but before them rose the sweet morning star, with a message of comfort and hope to those hearts so sorely tried.

H. L. HAVELL, *Stories from the Aeneid*

THE WANDERINGS OF ODYSSEUS

ODYSSEUS was the king of the rocky isle of Ithaca, where he lived with his wife Penelope and his son Telemachus. When Agamemnon summoned the Greek princes to the war against Troy, Odysseus, to escape going, feigned madness, ploughing the sands and sowing salt. Palamedes, however, discovered the imposture, for he laid Telemachus in the furrow and Odysseus turned the plough aside to save his infant son. At the siege of Troy his valour and his craft were of the greatest assistance to the Greeks, and, as you have read, it was by his stratagem of the wooden horse that Troy was ultimately captured.

After the fall of Troy the Greek heroes set sail for home, but none suffered so many hardships as Odysseus. For ten years he had fought at Troy, but it was ten years more before he came to Ithaca. During this time he passed through the adventures which are recorded in Homer's poem, the *Odyssey*. You may have heard of him as Ulysses, the name by which he is known in Latin poetry.

THE LOTUS-EATERS

AFTER leaving Troy, Odysseus first sailed to the coast of Thrace, and collected a rich booty in a sudden raid on the district. But while his men lingered to enjoy the first-fruits of their spoil, the wild tribes of the neighbourhood rallied their forces, and falling upon the invaders, while they were engaged in a drunken revel, drove them with great slaughter to their ships. No sooner had they put to sea than a wild tempest came down upon them from the north, and drove them to seek shelter again on the mainland, where they lay for two days and nights in constant dread of another attack from the injured Thracians. On the third day they set sail again, and got as far as Malea, the southernmost headland of Greece. Here they were again driven from their course.

H. L. HAVELL, *Stories from the Odyssey*

Nine days our fleet the uncertain tempest bore
Far in wide ocean, and from sight of shore :
The tenth we touch'd, by various errors toss'd,
The land of Lotus and the flowery coast.
We climb'd the beach, and springs of water found,
Then spread our hasty banquet on the ground.
Three men were sent, deputed from the crew
(A herald one) the dubious coast to view,
And learn what habitants possess'd the place.
They went, and found a hospitable race :
Not prone to ill, nor strange to foreign guest,
They eat, they drink, and nature gives the feast :
The trees around them all their food produce ;
Lotus the name : divine, nectareous juice !
(Thence call'd Lotophagi) ; which whoso tastes,
Insatiate riots in the sweet repasts,
Nor other home, nor other care intends,
But quits his house, his country, and his friends.
The three we sent, from off the enchanting ground
We dragg'd reluctant, and by force we bound :
The rest in haste forsook the pleasing shore,
Or, the charm tasted, had return'd no more.
Now placed in order on their banks, they sweep
The sea's smooth face, and cleave the hoary deep :
With heavy hearts we labour through the tide,
To coasts unknown, and oceans yet untried.

ALEXANDER POPE, *The Odyssey*

THE LOTUS-EATERS

" Courage ! " he said, and pointed toward the land,
" This mounting wave will roll us shoreward soon."
In the afternoon they came unto a land
In which it seemed always afternoon.
All round the coast the languid air did swoon,
Breathing like one that hath a weary dream.
Full-faced above the valley stood the moon ;
And like a downward smoke, the slender stream
Along the cliff to fall and pause and fall did seem.

A land of streams ! some, like a downward smoke,
Slow-dropping veils of thinnest lawn, did go ;
And some thro' wavering lights and shadows broke,
Rolling a slumbrous sheet of foam below.
They saw the gleaming river seaward flow
From the inner land : far off, three mountain-tops,
Three silent pinnacles of aged snow,
Stood sunset-flush'd : and, dew'd with showery drops,
Up-clomb the shadowy pine above the woven copse.

The charmed sunset linger'd low adown
In the red West : thro' mountain clefts the dale
Was seen far inland, and the yellow down
Border'd with palm, and many a winding vale
And meadow, set with slender galingale ;
A land where all things always seem'd the same !
And round about the keel with faces pale,
Dark faces pale against that rosy flame,
The mild-eyed melancholy Lotus-eaters came.

Branches they bore of that enchanted stem,
Laden with flower and fruit, whereof they gave
To each, but whoso did receive of them,

And taste, to him the gushing of the wave
Far far away did seem to mourn and rave
On alien shores ; and if his fellow spake,
His voice was thin, as voices from the grave ;
And deep-asleep he seem'd, yet all awake,
And music in his ears his beating heart did make.

They sat them down upon the yellow sand,
Between the sun and moon upon the shore ;
And sweet it was to dream of Fatherland,
Of child, and wife, and slave ; but evermore
Most weary seem'd the sea, weary the oar,
Weary the wandering fields of barren foam.
Then some one said, " We will return no more ; "
And all at once they sang, " Our island home
Is far beyond the wave ; we will no longer roam."

LORD TENNYSON, *The Lotus-eaters*

THE LAND OF THE CYCLOPES

COASTING on all that night by unknown and out-of-the-way shores, they came by daybreak to the land where the Cyclopes dwell, a sort of giant shepherds that neither sow nor plough, but the earth untilled produces for them rich wheat and barley and grapes, yet they have neither bread nor wine ; nor know the arts of cultivation, nor care to know them ; for they live each man to himself, without laws or government, or anything like a state or kingdom, but their dwellings are in caves, on the steep heads of mountains, every man's household governed by his own caprice, or not governed at all, their wives and children as lawless as themselves, none caring for others, but each doing as he or she thinks good. Ships or boats they have none, nor artificers to make them, no trade or commerce, or wish to visit other shores ; yet they have convenient places for harbours and for shipping. Here Ulysses with a chosen party of twelve followers landed to explore what sort of men dwelt there, whether hospitable and friendly to strangers, or altogether wild and savage, for as yet no dwellers appeared in sight.

The first sign of habitation which they came to was a giant's cave, rudely fashioned, but of a size which betokened the vast proportions of its owner, the pillars which supported it being the bodies of huge oaks or pines, in the natural state of the tree, and all about showed more marks of strength and skill in whoever built it. Ulysses, entering in, admired the savage contrivances and artless structure of the place, and longed to see the tenant of so outlandish a mansion; but well conjecturing that gifts would have more avail in extracting courtesy than strength could succeed in forcing it, from such a one as he expected to find the inhabitant, he resolved to flatter his hospitality with a present of Greek wine, of which he had store in twelve great vessels; so strong that no one ever drank it without an infusion of twenty parts of water to one of wine, yet the fragrance of it even then so delicious, that it would have vexed a man who smelled it to abstain from tasting it; but whoever tasted it, it was able to raise his courage to the height of heroic deeds.

Taking with them a goatskin flagon full of this precious liquor, they ventured into the recesses of the cave. Here they pleased themselves a whole day with beholding the giant's kitchen, where the flesh of sheep and goats lay strewed, his dairy where goat-milk stood ranged in troughs and pails, his pens where he kept his live animals; but those he had driven forth to pasture with him when he went out in the morning. While they were feasting their eyes with the sight of these curiosities, their ears were suddenly deafened with a noise like the falling of a house. It was the owner of the cave who had been abroad all day feeding his flock, as his custom was, in the mountains, and now drove them home in the evening from pasture. He threw down a pile of fire-wood, which he had been gathering against supper-time, before the mouth of the cave, which occasioned the crash they heard. The Grecians hid themselves in the remote parts of the cave, at sight of the uncouth monster. It was Polyphemus, the largest and savagest of the Cyclopes, who boasted himself to be the son of Poseidon. He looked more like a mountain crag than a man, and to his brutal body he had a brutish mind answerable. He drove his flock, all that gave milk, to the interior of the cave, but left the rams and the he-goats without. Then taking up a stone, so massy that twenty oxen could not have drawn it, he placed it at the mouth of the cave, to defend the entrance, and sat him down to milk his ewes and his goats ; which done, he lastly kindled a fire, and throwing his great eye round the cave (for the Cyclopes have no more than one eye, and that placed in the middle of their forehead), by the glimmering light he discerned some of Ulysses' men.

" Ho, guests, what are you ? merchants or wandering thieves ? " he bellowed out in a voice which took from them all power to reply, it was so astounding.

Only Ulysses summoned resolution to answer, that they came neither for plunder nor traffic, but were Grecians who had lost their way, returning from Troy ; which famous city, under the conduct of Agamemnon, the renowned son of Atreus, they had sacked, and laid level with the ground. Yet now they prostrated themselves humbly before his feet, whom they acknowledged to be mightier than they, and besought him that he would bestow the rites of hospitality upon them, for that Zeus was the avenger of wrongs done to strangers, and would fiercely resent any injury which they might suffer.

" Fool," said the Cyclops, " to come so far to preach

to me the fear of the gods. We Cyclopes care not for your Zeus, whom you fable to be nursed by a goat, nor any of your blessed ones. We are stronger than they, and dare bid open battle to Zeus himself, though you and all your fellows of the earth join with him." And he bade them tell him where their ship was, in which they came, and whether they had any companions. But Ulysses, with a wise caution, made answer, that they had no ship or companions, but were unfortunate men whom the sea, splitting their ship in pieces, had dashed upon his coast, and they alone had escaped. He replied nothing, but gripping two of the nearest of them, as if they had been no more than children, he dashed their brains out against the earth, and (shocking to relate) tore in pieces their limbs, and devoured them, yet warm and trembling, making a lion's meal of them, lapping the blood : for the Cyclopes are *man-eaters*, and esteem human flesh to be a delicacy far above goat's or kid's ; though by reason of their abhorred customs few men approach their coast except some stragglers, or now and then a shipwrecked mariner. At a sight so horrid, Ulysses and his men were like distracted people. He, when he had made an end of his wicked supper, drained a draught of goat's milk down his prodigious throat, and lay down and slept among his goats. Then Ulysses drew his sword, and half resolved to thrust it with all his might in at the bosom of the sleeping monster ; but wiser thoughts restrained him, else they had there without help all perished, for none but Polyphemus himself could have removed that mass of stone which he had placed to guard the entrance. So they were constrained to abide all that night in fear.

When day came the Cyclops awoke, and kindling a fire, made his breakfast of two other of his unfortunate prisoners, then milked his goats as he was accustomed.

and pushing aside the vast stone, and shutting it again when he had done, upon the prisoners, with as much ease as a man opens and shuts a quiver's lid, he let out his flock, and drove them before him with whistlings (as sharp as winds in storms) to the mountains.

Then Ulysses, of whose strength and cunning the Cyclops seems to have had as little heed as of an infant's, being left alone, with the remnant of his men which the Cyclops had not devoured, gave manifest proof how far manly wisdom excels brutish force. He chose a stake from among the wood which the Cyclops had piled up for firing, in length and thickness like a mast, which he sharpened and hardened in the fire, and selected four men, and instructed them what they should do with this stake, and made them perfect in their parts.

When the evening was come, the Cyclops drove home his sheep; and as fortune directed it, either of purpose, or that his memory was overruled by the gods to his hurt (as in the issue is proved), he drove the males of his flock, contrary to his custom, along with the dams into the pens. Then shutting to the stone of the cave, he fell to his horrible supper. When he had dispatched two more of the Grecians, Ulysses waxed bold with the contemplation of his project, and took a bowl of Greek wine, and merrily dared the Cyclops to drink.

"Cyclops," he said, "take a bowl of wine from the hand of your guest; it may serve to digest the man's flesh that you have eaten, and show what drink our ship held before it went down. All I ask in recompense, if you find it good, is to be dismissed in a whole skin. Truly you must look to have few visitors, if you observe this new custom of eating your guests."

The brute took and drank, and vehemently enjoyed the taste of wine, which was new to him, and swilled again at the flagon, and entreated for more, and prayed

Ulysses to tell him his name, that he might bestow a gift upon the man who had given him such brave liquor. The Cyclopes (he said) had grapes, but this rich juice (he swore) was simply divine. Again Ulysses plied him with the wine, and the fool drank it as fast as he poured out, and again he asked the name of his benefactor, which Ulysses cunningly dissembling, said, " My name is Noman ; my kindred and friends in my own country call me Noman." " Then," said the Cyclops, " this is the kindness I will show thee, Noman ; I will eat thee last of all thy friends." He had scarce expressed his savage kindness when the fumes of the strong wine overcame him, and he reeled down upon the floor and sank into a dead sleep.

Ulysses watched his time, while the monster lay insensible, and heartening up his men, they placed the sharp end of the stake in the fire till it was heated red-hot, and some god gave them a courage beyond that which they were used to have, and the four men with difficulty bored the sharp end of the huge stake, which they had heated red-hot, right into the eye of the drunken cannibal, and Ulysses helped to thrust it in with all his might, still farther and farther, with effort, as men bore with an auger, till the scalded blood gushed out, and the eyeball smoked, as the burning rafter broke in it, and the eye hissed, as hot iron hisses when it is plunged into water.

He, waking, roared with the pain so loud that all the cavern broke into claps like thunder. They fled, and dispersed into corners. He plucked the burning stake from his eye, and hurled the wood madly about the cave. Then he cried out with a mighty voice for his brethren the Cyclopes, that dwelt hard by in caverns upon hills ; they hearing the terrible shout came flocking from all parts to enquire what ailed Polyphemus ? and what cause he had for making such horrid clamours in the night-time to break their sleep ? if his fright proceeded

from any mortal ? if strength or craft had given him his
death's blow ? He made answer from within that Noman
had hurt him, Noman had killed him, Noman was with
him in the cave. They replied, " If no man has hurt
thee, and no man is with thee, then thou art alone, and
the evil that afflicts thee is from the hand of heaven,
which none can resist or help." So they left him and
went their way, thinking that some disease troubled him.
He, blind and ready to split with the anguish of the pain,
went groaning up and down in the dark to find the door-
way, which when he found, he removed the stone, and
sat in the threshold, feeling if he could lay hold on any
man going out with the sheep, which (the day now
breaking) were beginning to issue forth to their accustomed pastures. But Ulysses, whose first artifice, in
giving himself that ambiguous name, had succeeded so
well with the Cyclops, was not of a wit so gross to be
caught by that palpable device. But casting about in his
mind all the ways which he could contrive for escape (no
less than all their lives depending on the success), at last
he thought of this expedient. He made knots of the
osier twigs upon which the Cyclops commonly slept,
with which he tied the fattest and fleeciest of the rams
together, three in a rank, and under the belly of the middle
ram he tied a man, and himself last, wrapping himself
fast with both his hands in the rich wool of one, the
fairest of the flock.

And now the sheep began to issue forth very fast ;
the males went first, the females unmilked stood by,
bleating and requiring the hand of their shepherd in
vain to milk them ; their full udders sore with being
unempted, but he much sorer with the loss of sight.
Still as the males passed, he felt the backs of those fleecy
fools, never dreaming that they carried his enemies under
their bellies ; so they passed on till the last ram came

loaded with his wool and Ulysses together. He stopped that ram and felt him, and had his hand once in the hair of Ulysses, yet knew it not, and he chid the ram for being last, and spoke to it as if it understood him, and asked it whether it did not wish that its master had his eye again, which that abominable Noman with his execrable rout had put out, when they had got him down with wine; and he willed the ram to tell him whereabouts in the cave his enemy lurked, that he might dash his brains and strew them about, to ease his heart of that tormenting revenge which rankled in it. After a deal of such foolish talk to the beast he let it go.

When Ulysses found himself free, he let go his hold, and assisted in disengaging his friends. The rams which had befriended them they carried off with them to the ships, where their companions with tears in their eyes received them, as men escaped from death. They plied their oars, and set their sails, and when they were got as far off shore as a voice would reach, Ulysses cried out to the Cyclops: " Cyclops, thou should'st not have so much abused thy monstrous strength, as to devour thy guests. Zeus by my hand sends thee requital to pay thy savage inhumanity." The Cyclops heard, and came forth enraged, and in his anger he plucked a fragment of a rock, and threw it with blind fury at the ships: it narrowly escaped lighting upon the bark in which Ulysses sat, but with the fall it raised so fierce an ebb, as bore back the ship till it almost touched the shore. " Cyclops," said Ulysses, " if any ask thee who imposed on thee that unsightly blemish in thine eye, say it was Ulysses, son of Laertes: the King of Ithaca am I called, the waster of cities." Then they crowded sail, and beat the old sea, and forth they went with a forward gale.

CHARLES LAMB, *The Adventures of Ulysses*

AEAEA, THE ISLE OF CIRCE

AFTER leaving the land of the Cyclopes they came to the island of Aeolia, where dwelt Aeolus, the king of the winds. Here they remained a month and were hospitably entertained, and at their departure Aeolus secretly gave Odysseus a leathern bag in which all contrary winds were securely tied up, so that only the favouring west wind might speed them on. But on the tenth day, when well within sight of their beloved Ithaca, Odysseus, worn out with his long vigil at the main-sheet, dropped asleep. It was an evil opportunity for the curious crew, who were burning to know what was contained in the leathern bag that their commander had stored below so carefully. Within a trice the Bag of the Winds was cut, letting loose on them havoc and destruction.

They fared back to King Aeolus, and humbly begged his help once more. But he would not a second time labour to imprison the winds for men on whom the gods had obviously laid a curse of foolishness ; and they had to sail away unfriended. For six days they rowed hard against adverse weather ; and on the seventh their evil fortune lured them to the land of the Laestrygonians. Not one of the ships that entered the harbour ever came out again. Only Odysseus and his men, who lay outside awaiting them, were saved from the hands of that cruel race.

On went the single ship till it came to the isle of Aeaea, where it ran smoothly into a fair haven. The crew landed in safety, and for two days and nights they rested on the shore, Odysseus himself shooting them venison for their food. In all this time no human creature had been seen ; but Odysseus in his explorations had seen one sign of habitation—a curl of smoke rising from an oaken coppice. That gave at least some hope of succour ;

but when he called his men to search the wood with him, he found that their courage had been completely broken. Their sufferings from the savage Cyclops and the Laestrygonians had taught them to fear the unknown rather than to hope from it ; and none would volunteer for the expedition. So a council was called, lots were cast, and those on whom the lots fell went off most unwillingly, led by Eurylochus.

The island lay low upon the sea, with only one hill-peak ; and when they climbed the hill the circling waters could be seen stretching away to the horizon's edge, without another glimpse of land. It would seem that they were utterly cut off : that there was no possible succour anywhere but in the mysterious valley below them ; and the knowledge spurred them to seek out the dweller in the wood, and so perhaps find help and counsel.

In a wide and shallow valley, where the oaks had been cleared away and the sun streamed hotly upon a southern slope, they came upon the house of Circe, daughter of the Sun. No human figure could be seen :

> But beasts alone,
> Hill-wolves and lions, over whom the witch
> With evil drugs had her enchantment thrown.[1]

Even these creatures made no sound to break the silence that was like a menace, while the sailors stopped awestruck at the sight. The great house, with its many halls and shining marble pillars, fascinated their sight ; and the strange beasts which leapt and fawned around them seemed to invite them to enter. But while they stood in doubt, dreading to advance and yet withheld from flight by some impalpable, resistless power, the sound of a sweet voice rose upon the air. Softly at first it floated out to them, in trembling notes ; and they stole

[1] From Professor J. W. Mackail's translation of the *Odyssey*.

forward, drawn by the exquisite melody, until they stood upon the very threshold of Circe's house.

Circe came forward to welcome them, and with sweet words and fluttering movements of her soft hands, she brought them in and bade them sit ; and busied herself, with swift and stealthy eagerness, to mix and pour a luscious drink of Pramnian wine and honey. But before she gave the cup into their hands, she furtively dropped into it one of her secret baneful drugs ; and as they greedily drank, their human shape was instantly transformed to that of swine.

One of the crew, however, had not entered ; and when his comrades did not return, he ran back to the ship to tell of what had happened.

> " We went, Ulysses ! (such was thy command)
> Through the lone thicket and the desert land.
> A palace in a woody vale we found,
> Brown with dark forests, and with shades around.
> A voice celestial echoed through the dome,
> Or nymph or goddess, chanting to the loom.
> Access we sought, nor was access denied :
> Radiant she came : the portals open'd wide :
> The goddess mild invites the guests to stay :
> They blindly follow where she leads the way.
> I only wait behind of all the train :
> I waited long, and eyed the doors in vain :
> The rest are vanish'd, none repass'd the gate,
> And not a man appears to tell their fate." [1]

Odysseus, suspecting some evil, slung on his sword, seized his bow, and sped away to Circe's house. But suddenly in his path stood the god Hermes, messenger of Zeus, in the likeness of a handsome youth. The god held up an

---

[1] From Pope's translation of the *Odyssey*. The interpolation of these lines is the present editor's.

arresting hand, and then foretold all that should befall Odysseus in Circe's house, thinking to deter him. But when he would persist in the attempt to save his men, the god gave Odysseus a plant that should be an antidote to Circe's poison.

Below her courtesy an evil intent was lurking, as Odysseus knew too well ; and presently she served to him the same poisoned drink with which she had bewitched his men. But the plant of moly that Hermes had given him made him proof against her drugs. The wine failed of its effect, and Circe, angrily taking her wand, smote Odysseus with it, crying, " Be gone now to the sty and couch among your band."

Her mischievous purpose faded on the instant, and she became full of fawning admiration and wonder. Her malice was changed, but something even more dangerous took its place. She began with sweet words to smooth away Odysseus' anger, fondling him and begging him to remain with her and be her husband. But Odysseus remembered the warning of the god, and at first he would not yield. He was sullen and suspicious, and would not answer her gently until she had sworn to release his men.

> Thereat immediately
> Out through the palace, rod in hand, went she,
> And opened the sty-doors and drave them out
> Resembling swine of nine years old to see.
>
> Thereafter all in front of her stood they,
> While she passed down along their whole array,
> Smearing another drug on each of them ;
> And off their limbs the bristles fell away,
>
> That the first baleful drug from Circe's store
> Had made to grow upon them : and once more
> Men they became, and younger were to see
> And taller far and goodlier than before.[1]

[1] From Professor J. W. Mackail's translation of the *Odyssey*.

Then the ship was hauled into a cave, and their companions were induced to come up to Circe's house, where they all joined in feasting and merriment. Cautious Eurylochus tried to dissuade them; but Odysseus would give no heed to his warning; and there followed a long interval of riotous pleasure over which Circe and the river-nymphs who were her handmaidens presided as queens. The days went by uncounted in luxurious ease; and if, in rare moments, Odysseus had an uneasy flash of memory, Circe's caressing voice would flatter and soothe him into complacence again, persuading him to stay yet a little longer.

For a whole year the thought of home and friends was driven away, while jollity filled out the indolent hours. But at last Odysseus claimed from Circe the fulfilment of her promise to send them safely back. . . . He would be sad at leaving her, he said, since the time had passed so pleasantly in her sunny island; but now his men are beginning to complain and he himself (though that he did not tell her) had suddenly grown weary and remorseful. It all seemed very simple; and he had not much misgiving. Circe had only to speak the word, that they might have safe convoy, and return to Ithaca. Her reply was of ominous import. Since they wished to go, she would not detain them; but let Odysseus summon all his courage:

> " Not against your will
> You and your fellows longer shall abide
> Within my house; but you must first fulfil
> Another journey yet, the house to see
> Of Hades and renowned Persephone." [1]

With the help of Circe, the dark and awesome journey to the nether world was accomplished, and there Odysseus held converse with the dead prophet Tiresias, who told

[1] From Professor J. W. Mackail's translation of the *Odyssey*.

him what he must do if he would reach Ithaca in safety. Then Odysseus returned to Aeaea, where Circe made him tell her all that had befallen him, and all that he had seen in the House of Hades ; and then she gave him directions for his homeward voyage. He was to beware of the Sirens, and of Scylla and Charybdis : but above all he must prevent his men from doing injury to the sacred Oxen of the Sun.

M. C. STURGEON, *Women of the Classics* (adapted)

OGYGIA, THE HOME OF CALYPSO

WHEN they neared Anthemousa, the flowery isle of the Sirens, Odysseus stopped the ears of all his men with wax, while he himself was firmly bound to the mast ; they passed between dread Scylla and Charybdis with the sacrifice of six men to the shark-like jaws of Scylla ; and then they came to Trinacria, the fair isle of Helios, whereon, as they drew near, they heard the lowing of oxen and the bleating of sheep. Here for a whole month they were detained by contrary winds, and when their store of provisions had come to an end, the crew, unmindful of the warning of Tiresias, seized some of the sacred Oxen of the Sun, while their commander slept. And when at last they sailed away they were smitten by an avenging storm sent by the wrathful Apollo and every one paid the penalty with his life, all save Odysseus, who was cast upon the shores of Ogygia, the home of the nymph Calypso.

Calypso dwelt alone in a great cavern :

The cave was brighten'd with a rising blaze ;
Cedar and frankincense, an odorous pile,
Flamed on the hearth, and wide perfumed the isle ;
While she with work and song the time divides,
And through the loom the golden shuttle guides.

Without the grot a various sylvan scene
Appear'd around, and groves of living green ;
Poplars and alders ever quivering play'd,
And nodding cypress form'd a fragrant shade ;
On whose high branches, waving with the storm,
The birds of broadest wing their mansions form—
The chough, the sea-mew, the loquacious crow—
And scream aloft, and skim the deeps below.
Depending vines the shelving cavern screen,
With purple clusters blushing through the green.
Four limpid fountains from the clefts distil ;
And every fountain pours a several rill,
In mazy windings wandering down the hill :
Where bloomy meads with vivid greens were crown'd,
And glowing violets threw odours round.
A scene, where, if a god should cast his sight,
A god might gaze, and wander with delight ! [1]

For seven years Odysseus lived in this enchanted island,
but at last the gods took pity on his sorrow and his longing,
and Hermes was sent to order Calypso to let him sail
home. His hardships, however, were not over, for his
enemy Poseidon wrecked the raft which he had so labori-
ously built, and it was sore spent and exhausted that he
reached the land of the Phaeacians. Here the shipwrecked
hero met the Princess Nausicaa as she played ball with
her maidens on the shore, and from kindly King Alcinous
and the gracious Queen Arete he received royal welcome
and hospitality and then safe convoy to Ithaca.

A. J. M.

THE RETURN OF ODYSSEUS

[During the long, unhappy years of Odysseus' absence,
his wife Penelope had prayed and hoped for his return,

[1] From Pope's translation of the *Odyssey*.

and all but despaired of ever seeing him again. Since the time of the fall of Troy she had been plagued by her kinsfolk to choose a husband to succeed Odysseus, long since presumed dead, and a host of ardent and needy suitors battened on her substance, each trying to force her to choose himself. Her young son, Telemachus, now grown to manhood, could do little to protect his mother, who had, however, kept the demands of her unwelcome wooers at bay for several years by a ruse worthy of Odysseus himself. She asked for a respite till she should have time to weave a shroud for her father-in-law.

> Thus then all of the day at the spacious loom she was
>   weaving ;
> During the night she unravelled the web with the torches
>   beside her.
> Three long years with her secret device she befooled the
>   Achaeans :
> Till, when the fourth year came, and as season was followed
>   by season,
> Then at the last (since one of her women, who knew it, had
>   told us),
> While at the loom her magnificent web she unravelled, we
>   caught her.
> Thus was she forced, though sorely unwilling, to finish her
>   labour.[1]

At length, however, Penelope in despair appoints a day on which she will name a successor to Odysseus.

Odysseus, meanwhile, has been brought to the hut of his swineherd, by the intervention of Athene, and there he and Telemachus are made known to each other, and conspire together to get rid of the parasites dwelling in their home, and put an end to the years of separation and unhappiness.]

The time had now arrived for the great trial of strength and skill of which Penelope had spoken, and which was to

[1] From H. B. Cotterill's translation of the *Odyssey*.

decide deeper and deadlier issues than those of marriage. Among the treasures which Odysseus had left behind him was a famous bow, which he had received as a gift in his youth. He who strung this bow, and shot an arrow through a line of axes set up in the hall, was to be rewarded by the hand of Penelope.

"Mother, it is time!" whispered Telemachus. Obeying the signal, Penelope, who had been sitting in the hall listening to the talk of the wooers, left her place, and ascending a steep staircase made her way to the store-room, which was situated at the farther end of the house. In her hand she carried a brazen key with a handle of ivory; and when she came to the door, she loosened the strap which served to draw the bolt from the outside, and inserting the key drew back the bolt. The double doors flew open with a crash, and the treasury with all its wealth was revealed. Great coffers of cedar-wood lined the walls, filled with fine raiment which her own hands had wrought. It was a cool and quiet retreat, dimly lighted, remote from all rude sounds, full of fragrant odours, and fit to guard the possessions of a prince. And there, hanging from a pin, and heedfully wrapped in its case, was seen the fatal bow. She took it down, and, sitting on one of the coffers, laid it on her knees, and gazed on it fondly with her eyes full of tears. How often had she seen it in the hands of Odysseus, when he went forth at sunrise to hunt the hare and the deer! How often had she taken it from him when he came back at evening loaded with the spoils of the chase! And now a keen shaft from this very bow was to cut the last tender cord of memory, and make her another man's wife!

With a heavy heart she took the bow with its quiver in her hands, and descending the staircase, re-entered the hall, followed by her maidens, who carried a chest containing the axes.

" Behold the bow, fair sirs ! " she said to the wooers, " and behold me, the prize for this fine feat of archery ! " Therewith she gave the bow to Eumaeus, who received it with tears ; and Philoetius wept likewise when he saw the treasured weapon of his lord. These signs of emotion stirred the anger of Antinous, who rebuked the herdsmen fiercely. " Peace, fools ! " he cried. " Peace, miserable churls ! Why pierce ye the heart of the lady with your howlings ? Has she not grief enough already ? Go forth and howl with the dogs outside, and we will make trial of the bow ; yet methinks it will be long ere anyone here shall string it."

" Anyone save thyself, thou wouldst say ! " rejoined Telemachus with a loud laugh. Then, seeing his mother regarding him with gentle reproach, he added : " 'Tis strange that I should feel so gay and light of heart at the moment when I am about to lose my mother. Zeus, methinks, has turned my brain, and made me laugh when I should weep. But come, ye bold wooers, which of you will be the first to enter the lists for this matchless prize, a lady without peer in all the land of Hellas ? Why sit ye thus silent ? Must I show you the way ? So be it, then ; and if I can bend the bow, and shoot an arrow straight, the prize shall be mine, and my mother shall abide here in her widowed state."

So saying he sprang up, flung off his cloak, and laid aside his sword. And first he made a long, shallow trench in the floor of the hall, and set up the axes with their double heads in a straight line, stamping down the earth about the handles to make all firm. Then he took the bow from Eumaeus ; it was a weighty and powerful weapon fashioned from the horns of an ibex, which were firmly riveted into a massive bridge, and great force was required to string it. Telemachus set the end against the floor, and strove with all his might to drive the string into its socket. Three times he tried and failed ; but the fourth time, making a great effort, he was on the point of succeeding, when his father nodded to him to desist. " Plague on it ! " cried Telemachus, laying the bow aside with an air of vexation, " must I be called a poltroon all my life, or is it that I have not yet attained the full measure of my strength ? Let the others now take their turn."

Then one by one the wooers rose up, in the order in which they sat, and tried to bend the bow. The first to essay it was Leiodes, a soothsayer, and a man of gentle and godly mind. But he was a soft liver, unpractised in all manly pastimes, and the bow was like iron in his white, womanish hands. " I fear that this bow will make an end of many a bold spirit," he said, little guessing how true his words were to prove ; " for better it were to die than to go away beaten and broken men, after all the long years of our wooing."

" Fie on thee ! " cried Antinous, " thinkest thou that there are no better men here than thou art ? Doubt not that one of those present shall bend the bow and win the lady." Then he called Melanthius, and bade him light a fire, and bring a ball of lard to anoint the bow and make it easier to bend. The lard was brought, and the wooers sat in turn by the fire, rubbing and anointing the bow, but all to no purpose. Only Antinous and Eurymachus still held back, each in the full assurance that he, and none other, should have strength to bend the bow.

Odysseus [in the disguise of a beggar] sat watching the wooers from his place at the upper end of the hall, and his heart misgave him when he thought of the appalling task which he had undertaken. He had acquitted himself like a hero in many a hard-fought field, but never in all his life had he faced such odds as these. While he thus mused, and weighed the chances in his mind, he saw Eumaeus and Philoetius leave the hall together, and pass out through the courtyard gate. Then a sudden thought struck him, and muttering to himself, " I must risk it," he rose and followed the two men. He found them talking together outside the courtyard fence, and in order to make trial of their temper he addressed them in these cautious terms : " Tell me truly, good friends, which side would ye take, if by some miracle Odysseus suddenly appeared in this house ? Would ye be for the wooers or for him ? "

Eumaeus and Philoetius with one voice protested that they were ready to hazard their lives for the rights of their master, whereupon Odysseus hesitated no longer, but answered : " The miracle has been wrought ; I am he ! After twenty years of toil and wandering Heaven hath brought me home. I have watched ye both, and I know that ye alone among all the thralls remain true to me. Only continue steadfast for this day, and your reward is assured. I will build houses for ye both, close to my own, and ye shall dwell there with your wives, as my friends and neighbours, equals in honour with Telemachus, my son."

The swineherd and neatherd listened with amazement, willing to believe, but still half in doubt ; but when Odysseus showed them a scar on his foot which they had seen many a time before, they were convinced, and embraced their old master with tears and cries of joy. Having allowed them some moments to indulge their feelings, Odysseus checked them with a warning gesture. " Take heed to yourselves," he said, " or your cries will betray us. And now mark what I shall tell you. I will go back to the house first, and do ye two follow me one by one. To thee, Philoetius, I give charge to make fast the gate of the courtyard, with bolt and with bar and with cord. And thou, Eumaeus, when the time comes, shalt bring the bow and place it in my hands, whether the wooers cry out on thee or not ; and when thou hast given me the bow, go straightway and command the women to make fast the doors of their apartments, and remain quiet by their work until I have finished what I have to do."

At the moment when Odysseus returned to his place in the hall, Eurymachus was just making a last attempt to bend the bow. " Out on it ! " he cried, finding all his efforts of no avail. " It is a shame to think how far beneath Odysseus we all are in the strength of our hands ; 'tis this that stings me, much more than the loss of the lady."

" Thou mistakest the cause," answered Antinous. " This day is the holy feast of the divine archer, Apollo, and doubtless he is jealous because we try our skill in his own art on his sacred day. Let us leave the axes where they stand, and try our fortune again to-morrow."

The proposal was received with general applause, and forthwith the whole company called loud for wine, and began drinking heavily to drown their disappointment. Odysseus watched the progress of the revel with grim satisfaction, and when the flushed faces and thick talk of the wooers showed that they were far gone in drunkenness he asked, with an air of deep humility, to be allowed to try his hand at stringing the bow. His request was greeted with a loud cry of contempt and indignation from all the wooers ; and Antinous especially was highly incensed, threatening him with dire pains and penalties for his presumption. Hereupon Penelope interposed, and rebuked Antinous for his violence. " Why should not the stranger try his skill with the rest ? " asked she. " Thinkest thou that the poor man will win me for his wife if he succeeds ? Sure am I that he is not so foolish as to entertain such a thought."

" 'Tis not for that," said Eurymachus, answering her. " He cannot be so mad as that. But what a shame to all this noble company if a houseless beggar should accomplish a feat which none of us was able to perform."

"Talk not of shame," replied Penelope with scorn. "Are ye not covered with shame already, by your foul deeds done in this house in the absence of its lord ? Give him the bow, I say ! And if he string it, by Apollo's grace, I will clothe him in a new cloak and doublet, and give him a sharp javelin to keep off dogs and men, and a two-edged sword, and sandals for his feet, and give him safe conduct to whatsoever place he desires to reach."

The decisive moment was at hand, and Telemachus saw the necessity of removing his mother from the scene of the approaching conflict. "Mother," he said in a tone of authority, "leave these things to me ; I am master here. Evening draws on, and it is time for thee to retire."

When Penelope had withdrawn, Eumaeus took the bow, and was about to carry it to Odysseus, but paused half-way, in doubt and alarm, for a perfect storm of threats and abuse assailed his ears. "Halt, thou dog ! Put down the bow ! Art thou tired of thy life ? " Appalled by the menacing cries of the wooers, the swineherd stood hesitating ; but Telemachus raised his voice, and commanded him instantly to deliver the bow to Odysseus. "I will teach thee," he said, "who is thy master ; thou shalt carry the marks of my hands to thy farm, if thou do not as I tell thee. Would that I could as easily drive the whole of this drunken rout from my doors ! "

"Well bragged, Sir Valiant ! " cried Antinous ; and all the wooers laughed boisterously when they heard him. Seizing his opportunity while their attention was thus diverted, Eumaeus came and placed the bow in the hands of Odysseus ; then, calling Eurycleia, he bade her make fast the door of the women's apartments. Meanwhile Philoetius secured the gates of the courtyard, and returning to his place sat watching the movements of Odysseus.

With anxious eyes the hero scrutinized the great weapon, turning it this way and that, to see if it had been injured by worms or natural decay. To his great joy he found that it was sound and untouched. Then, easily as a minstrel fastens a new cord to a lyre, without effort he strung the bow, and bending it made the string twang loud and clear, like the shrill voice of the swallow.

A hundred mocking eyes and sneering faces had been turned towards him, as he sat fingering the bow and weighing it in his hands ; but pale grew those faces now, and blank was that gaze. To add to their terror, at this moment a loud peal of thunder shook the house. Filled with high courage by the happy omen, Odysseus took an arrow, and, fitting it to the string, sent it with sure aim from the place where he sat along the whole line of axe-heads, from the first to the last.

" Telemachus," he said, " thy guest hath not shamed thee. My hand is firm, and mine eye is true, poor worn-out wanderer though I be. Now let us give these fair guests their supper, and afterwards entertain them with music and with dancing, which are the fit accompaniment of a feast."

Then he beckoned to his son to draw near ; and Telemachus made haste, and came and stood by his father's side, armed with sword and lance.

Stripping off his rags, and girding them round his waist, Odysseus took the quiver, and poured out all the arrows on the ground at his feet. " Now guide my hand, Apollo," he cried, " and make sure mine aim, for this time I will shoot at a mark which never man hit before."

Therewith he bent his bow again, and pointed the arrow at Antinous, who just at that moment was raising a full goblet of wine to his lips. Little thought that proud and insolent man, as the wine gleamed red before him, that he had tasted his last morsel, and drunk his last

ɪ

drop. He was in the prime of his manhood, surrounded by his friends, and in the midst of a joyous revel ; who would dream of death and doom in such an hour ? Yet at that very instant he felt a sharp, sudden pang, and fell back in his seat, pierced through the throat by the arrow of Odysseus. The blood poured from his nostrils, he let fall the cup, and spurning the table with his feet in his agony he overset it, and the bread and meat were scattered on the floor.

Then arose a wild clamour and uproar among the wooers, and starting from their seats they eagerly sought for the weapons which were wont to hang along the walls ; but not a spear, not a shield, was to be seen ; for they had been secretly removed by Telemachus. Finding themselves thus baffled, they turned furiously on Odysseus, shouting, " Down with the knave ! " " Hew him in pieces ! " " Fling his carcass to the vultures ! " As yet they had not recognized him, and they thought that he had slain Antinous by mischance.

They were soon undeceived. " Ye dogs ! " he cried, in a terrible voice, " long have ye made my house into a den of thieves, thinking that I had died long ago in a distant land. Ye have devoured my living, and wooed my wife, and mishandled my servants, having no fear of god or man before your eyes. But now are ye all fallen into the pit which ye have digged, and are fast bound in the bonds of death."

Like beaten hounds, that dastardly crew cowered before the man whom they had wronged, and every heart quaked with fear. Presently Eurymachus stood forward, and tried to make terms for them all. " If thou be indeed Odysseus," he said, " thou speakest justly concerning the evil doings of the wooers. And there lies the cause of the mischief, Antinous, struck down by thy righteous hand. He it was who sought to slay Telemachus, that he might usurp thy place, and make himself king in Ithaca. But now that he is gone to his own place, let us, the rest, find favour in thy sight. And as for thy possessions which have been wasted, we will pay thee back out of our own goods, as much as thou shalt require."

But there were no signs of relenting on that stern, set face. "Talk not to me of payment," he answered, with a brow as black as night; "ye shall pay me with your lives, every one of you. Fight, if ye will, or die like sheep. Not one of you shall escape."

Thus driven to extremity, Eurymachus drew his sword, and shouting to the others to follow his example he picked up a table to serve him as a shield, and raising his war-cry rushed at Odysseus. In the midst of his onset an arrow struck him in the liver, and he fell doubled up over a table, smiting the floor with his forehead. Then he rolled over with a groan, and his eyes grew dim in death.

Before Odysseus could fix another arrow to the string, Amphinomus was upon him, with sword uplifted to slay him. Telemachus saw his father's peril, and thrust Amphinomus in the back with his spear. The fall of their leaders arrested the advance of the wooers, and they drew back in a body to the lower end of the hall. Leaving the spear in the body of the fallen man, Telemachus ran to fetch armour for himself and Odysseus, and the two herdsmen. Quickly he brought shields and helmets and lances for the four, and they arrayed themselves and took their stand together on the platform.

While these preparations were in progress, Odysseus continued showering his arrows among the huddled troop of terrified men; and at every shot one of the wooers fell. At last Melanthius, the goatherd, made a desperate effort to save his party. Assisted by several of the wooers, he climbed up the wall of the banquet-room, and made his exit through the open timbers at the top into a narrow passage which gave access to the inner part of the house. Presently he returned, laden with spears and shields and helmets, which he had found in the chamber where they had been stored away by Telemachus.

What was the dismay of Odysseus when he saw his enemies arming themselves with spear and shield, and brandishing long lances in their hands ! " Telemachus ! " he cried, " we are betrayed ! The women have sold us to the wooers." " Alas ! I have erred," answered Telemachus, " for I left the door of the armoury open, and one of them has observed it."

While they thus debated, Eumaeus saw the goatherd making his way out of the hall again by the same exit. " It is the traitor Melanthius," he whispered ; " now have we need of prompt action, or we are all undone."

Odysseus had now recovered his courage, and he issued his orders without losing another moment. " Go thou with the neatherd," he said to Eumaeus, " and seize that villain before he has time to return. Bind him hand and foot, and come back with all speed to the hall."

At the side of the hall, close to the platform where Odysseus and his party were stationed, there was a door leading into the passage already mentioned. Through this the two men passed, and made their way stealthily to the armoury. There they waited on either side of the door for Melanthius, whom they heard moving within. Before long he came out, bearing in one hand a helmet, and in the other an old battered shield, once the property of Laertes. Together they fell upon him, dragged him down by the hair, and having bound him tight with a long cord they hauled him up to a beam of the roof and left him hanging. " Long and sweet be thy slumbers, goatherd ! " said Eumaeus as he contemplated his work, " thou hast a soft bed such as thou lovest. Rest there till the morning light shall call thee to make breakfast for the wooers."

When they returned to the hall they found that a new ally had joined their party, in the person of Mentor, the old friend of Odysseus. No one saw when he came hither ; but there he was, and right glad they were to see him. Very different were the feelings of the wooers when they saw their enemies thus reinforced, and one of them, named Agelaus, cried out upon Mentor, and threatened him, saying : " Give place, rash man, or thou wilt bring destruction on thyself and all thy house."

When he heard that, Mentor was wroth, and rebuked Odysseus as slow of hand and cold of heart. " Why standest thou idle ? " he cried. " Get thee to thy weapons, and finish the work which thou hast to do, if thou art verily that Odysseus who wrought such havoc among the Trojans in the nine years' war."

With these words the supposed Mentor vanished as mysteriously as he had appeared, and a little swallow was seen darting hither and thither among the smoke-blackened beams of the roof.

The wooers understood not in whose presence they had been, and thinking that Mentor had fled before their threats, they took courage again, and prepared to make a fresh assault. Agelaus now took the lead, and at his command six of them advanced and hurled their spears. But they were all dazed with drink, and weakened by long habits of loose indulgence, and not one of their weapons took effect.

" Now hurl ye your spears ! " shouted Odysseus, and the four lances flew, and four wooers bit the dust. At the next discharge from the wooers Telemachus received a slight wound on the wrist, and Eumaeus was similarly injured on the shoulder by the spear of the brutal Ctesippus. A moment after Ctesippus himself was struck down by the lance of Philoetius, who mocked him as he fell, saying : " There is for the ox-foot which thou didst lately bestow on Odysseus, thou noisy railer ! "

And so the great fight went on, and at every cast of the spear Odysseus and his men added another to the list of the slain.   Seeing their numbers dwindling fast, the wretched remnant of the wooers lost heart altogether and huddled together like sheep at the end of the hall.   To complete their discomfiture a terrible voice was suddenly heard in the air, and a gleam as from a bright shield was seen high up among the rafters.   " 'Tis Athene herself come to our aid ! " cried Odysseus ; " advance and make an end of them.   Athene is on our side ! "   Forthwith they all sprang down from the platform and charged the wooers, of whom some dozen still remained alive.   What followed was not a battle, but a massacre.   Like a drove of kine plunging frantically over a field, tortured by the sting of the hovering gadfly—like a flock of small birds scattered by the sudden swoop of a falcon—the panic-stricken wooers fled hither and thither through the hall, seeking shelter behind pillars and under tables from the blows which rained upon them.   But vain was their flight. In a very short time the last of that guilty band was sent to his account, and the great act of vengeance was completed.

H. L. HAVELL, *Stories from the Odyssey*

GREEK TRAGEDY

IN the Introduction you read that Philip Wakem said he would have liked to have been a Greek and have come home and written plays. The Greeks were fond of the theatre, and many of their plays have come down to us. Their greatest theatre was built on the southern slope of the steep hill on whose summit stood the Acropolis of Athens.

This theatre consisted of three parts—the part occupied by the spectators, which was semicircular in form, hewn out of the solid rock, the seats ascending, tier above tier, up the side of the hill, and capable of accommodating thirty thousand people ; the stage, for the actors ; and the orchestra, or dancing-place. The whole was open to the sky, and both actors and audience were exposed to the fierce rays of the southern sun, and occasional showers of rain, happily rare in that climate. The acting began in the morning, and tragedy succeeded tragedy all day long. Defended from the weather by broad-brimmed hats, and, doubtless, provided with some form of refreshment, the vast crowd sat patiently on from morning till evening, while the grand procession of their national legends moved slowly in solemn pageant before them.

H. L. HAVELL, Stories from Greek Tragedy

The following are some of the stories told by the Greek dramatists in their plays :

ANTIGONE

ANTIGONE was the daughter of the old King Oedipus of Thebes. After a time heavy troubles came upon him, and he was driven away from his kingdom, and sent to wander forth a blind old man, scorned and pointed at by all. Then it was that his faithful daughter showed true affection for him. She might have remained at Thebes with her brother Eteocles, who had been made king in his father's place, but she chose instead to wander forth with the forlorn old man, fallen from his kingly state, and absolutely begging his bread. The great Athenian poet Sophocles began one of his tragedies with showing the blind old King leaning upon Antigone's arm, and asking :

> Tell me, thou daughter of a blind old man,
> Antigone, to what land are we come,
> Or to what city ? Who the inhabitants
> Who with a slender pittance will relieve
> Even for a day the wandering Oedipus ?

The place to which they had come was in Attica, near the city of Colonus. It was a lovely grove—

> All the haunts of Attic ground,
> Where the matchless coursers bound,
> Boast not, through their realms of bliss,
> Other spot so fair as this.
> Frequent down this greenwood dale
> Mourns the warbling nightingale,
> Nestling 'mid the thickest screen
> Of the ivy's darksome green,
> Or where each empurpled shoot
> Drooping with its myriad fruit,
> Curl'd in many a mazy twine,
> Droops the never-trodden vine.

This beautiful grove was sacred to the Eumenides, or avenging goddesses, and it was therefore a sanctuary where no foot might tread ; but near it the exiled king was allowed to take up his abode, and was protected by the great Athenian King, Theseus. There his other daughter, Ismene, joined him, and after a time his elder son, Polynices, arrived.

Polynices had been expelled from Thebes by his brother Eteocles, and had been wandering through Greece seeking aid to recover his rights. He had collected an army, and was come to take leave of his father and sisters ; and at the same time to entreat his sisters to take care that, if he should fall in battle, they would prevent his corpse from being left unburied ; for the Greeks believed that till the funeral rites were performed, the spirit went wandering restlessly up and down upon the banks of the dark stream of the Underworld, unable to enter the home of the dead. Antigone solemnly promised to him that he should not be left without these last rites. Before long, old Oedipus was killed by lightning, and the two sisters returned to Thebes.

The united armies of the seven chiefs against Thebes came on, led by Polynices. Eteocles sallied out to meet them, and there was a terrible battle, ending in all the seven chiefs being slain, and the two brothers, Eteocles and Polynices, were killed by one another in single combat. Creon, the uncle, who thus became king, had always been on the side of Eteocles, and therefore commanded that, whilst this younger brother was entombed with all due solemnities, the body of the elder should be left upon the battlefield to be torn by dogs and vultures, and that whosoever durst bury it should be treated as a rebel and traitor to the State.

This was the time for the sister to remember her oath to her dead brother. The more timid Ismene would have dissuaded her, but she answered :

> To me no sufferings have that hideous form
> Which can affright me from a glorious death.

And she crept forth by night, amid all the horrors of the deserted field of battle, and herself covered with loose earth the corpse of Polynices. The barbarous uncle

caused it to be taken up and again exposed, and a watch
was set at some little distance. Again Antigone

> Was seen, lamenting shrill with plaintive notes,
> Like the poor bird that sees her lonely nest
>   Spoil'd of her young.

Again she heaped dry dust with her own hands over the
body, and poured forth the libations of wine that formed
an essential part of the ceremony. She was seized by the
guard, and led before Creon. She boldly avowed her
deed, and in spite of the supplications of Ismene, she was
put to death, a sufferer for her noble and pious deeds ; and
with this only comfort :

> Glowing at my heart
> I feel this hope, that to my father, dear,
> And dear to thee, my mother, dear to thee,
> My brother, I shall go.

C. M. YONGE, *A Book of Golden Deeds*

IPHIGENEIA

THE fleet of a thousand ships, that was to carry the
Greeks to the siege of Troy, assembled at Aulis, in the
narrow strait between Euboea and the mainland of Greece,
and lay there waiting for a favourable wind. But the days
went by, lengthening into weeks, and still the winds were
contrary. All hearts were growing weary, when a strange
portent appeared, full of dark meaning. On a lofty rock,
in sight of the whole host of Greeks, two eagles were seen,
feasting on the body of a hare. What did this mean ? Was
it not a sign sent by Artemis to warn the princes ?

Not in vain was the warning sent. For months the fleet
lay idle, waiting for a fair wind. Stores were exhausted
and thousands sat fasting and weary by their camp-fires.
Then loud murmurs began to rise against the brothers
Agamemnon and Menelaus, who had brought the great

army there to starve. At last Calchas, the priest and prophet of the Grecian host, gave clear utterance to the general complaint, and went about the camp crying that the gods were wroth and claimed a sacrifice. " They will have blood "—so ran the awful message—" the blood of a stainless maid, else must we remain here and perish."

" The blood of a stainless maid ! " The words reached Agamemnon's ears, and fell upon them like the voice of doom. " The curse ! The curse ! My daughter, O my daughter, pride of my home, light of mine eyes ! " he muttered, wringing his hands in agony. " They will take thy life, Iphigeneia, my own heart's darling ! " Long he resisted, vowing that all should perish rather than that a hair of her head should suffer harm. But when the army rose in open mutiny, and all the princes thronged round him with fierce looks, crying for blood, he gave way to the storm, bowed his head, and whispered : " Let it be done ! "

Bound hand and foot, her cries stifled by a gag, Iphigeneia was brought to the place of sacrifice, and laid upon the altar by the hands of those stern warrior chiefs. There she lay, robed as a princess, her eyes beseeching pity of her butchers. Will no heart melt, no hand be raised, in answer to that mute appeal ? Will none remember the day when he sat as a guest in her father's hall, and took the cup from her hands, and listened to the thrilling tones of her voice as she sang the sacred hymn to Zeus ? No, not one ; frantic fear has turned all hearts to stone. Only her father veils his face, that he may not see the death of his child.

[Just as the knife was falling to her throat Iphigeneia was carried off by Artemis.]

H. L. HAVELL, *Stories from Greek Tragedy*

THE RESCUE OF IPHIGENEIA

TEN years had passed in the siege of Troy, and Agamemnon returned home to Argos to die at the hands of his wife, Clytemnestra. His death, however, was avenged by his son, Orestes, who became a fugitive, seeking through many lands to expiate the crime of mother-murder. There had been laid upon him at last, as the only means to peace, the command of Apollo to make his way to the savage land of the Tauri. He was to seize and bring from the temple of Artemis there a certain statue of the goddess which had fallen from heaven long before, and which the people of the land were dishonouring by human sacrifice. Every stranger cast upon their shores was slain at the shrine of the goddess; and Orestes ran the risk of almost certain death in making the venture. But he had a solemn promise from Apollo; and the reward would be sweet indeed. He would be cleansed of the crime, and set free from those haunting shapes of remorse which sometimes drove him to madness. Moreover, he would rid the name of Hellas from the stain which lay upon its religion through the barbarous practices of the Tauri. So he and his devoted comrade, Pylades, sailed for those inhospitable waters.

But Destiny was guiding them to something stranger than they had either hoped or dreaded. For this wild land, fiercely guarded from approach by the Gateway of the Clashing Rocks, was the country to which Artemis had carried Iphigeneia from the altar in Aulis. And in the temple where they must seek the sacred statue, the daughter of Agamemnon was even now a priestess.

The two comrades are captured and brought before the priestess at the altar. There the brother and sister recognize each other.

Orestes and Pylades, after a wild exclamation each to

the other, stand listening in bewildered joy as Iphigeneia proceeds, relating the story of her rescue by Artemis, and calling upon her brother to come and save her from captivity. During the recital, they have had time to grasp the wonder of the things they have heard ; but no ray of truth has come to Iphigeneia. And when Orestes turns eagerly to embrace the sister so marvellously saved, she recoils in horror.

Iphigeneia, incredulous, thinks he is mocking her. She has been so long dead to love and happiness that she cannot believe that they have come to her at last, and that this is really her brother. She insists on proof of his identity ; and as he tells over the little homely signs by which she may know him, her doubt slips away and she clasps him in her arms.

They cling to each other, Iphigeneia oblivious of everything but her joy, and Orestes loth to recall her to a sense of their danger. Presently her thoughts come painfully back to it, fluttering wildly round each possibility of escape together, and seeing no way clear. But when Orestes tells her of his mission to carry off the statue of the goddess, the very magnitude of its daring clarifies her mind. She sees one way, and though it is not the way she had hoped, she is ready for the sacrifice. She must secure the statue, and Orestes must escape with it to Attica, as the god commands. For herself, her part will be to stay, and by every means prevent her brother from being followed. She is sure of success in this, and though it may mean death for her, it will be sweet to give herself for the peace of one so dear. But Orestes absolutely refuses to accept his life at such a price ; and they strain every nerve to contrive a scheme which will carry them to safety together. There is a suggestion to kill the King, but the woman who has been sheltered and protected by him will not hear of it. Again, they think of hiding in the temple until nightfall ; but that is impracticable, because the guards would see and capture them. And at last Iphigeneia, beating backward and forward over all the possible chances, sees a gleam of hope. Slowly and carefully she unfolds her plan. She will give out that the victims for the altar have come from Greece polluted with a mother's blood, and that they may not be offered to the goddess until they have been cleansed in the sea. The statue, she will say, is unclean too, since one of the captives has touched it ; and she will prevail upon the King to allow her to take it, with the victims, down to the seashore. The rest will be Orestes' task ; and as his ship with fifty rowers lies waiting for them in the little bay, they should be able to get away before Thoas can follow.

The scheme is at once subtle and daring, but it is their only hope of escape from awful peril ; and it is hastily resolved upon. Iphigeneia claims a promise of loyalty from her women, sends the prisoners away in charge of attendants, and goes into the temple for the statue. As she comes out again, bearing it in her hands, the King himself arrives. To his astonished questions, she answers as has been arranged, and no point is overlooked by her ingenuity. A herald should be sent before her, to clear the streets, and proclaim that no one must look out, or leave his house, for fear of pollution. Thoas himself, and his attendants, must veil their eyes when her procession passes ; and while she is gone, the King is to purge the temple with fire in preparation for her return. Lastly, if she be a long time away, the King need not be anxious, and she must not be disturbed : the cleansing must be thoroughly performed.

The King consents without a shadow of suspicion, impressed by her piety and forethought. The prisoners are led out, and as the procession moves away, Iphigeneia utters a prayer for help in her strategy and pardon for the deceit that she has practised on the King.

Thoas returns to the temple to carry out Iphigeneia's injunctions. Time slips by, bringing we know not what to the fugitives. Then there is a sudden shout; and a messenger comes running from the shore and cries for entrance to the temple. He batters upon the gates until Thoas throws them open, angry at the clamour.

In rapid and excited speech the man tells his errand. Let the King come at once, for he has been befooled. The cleansing was a fraud; the statue has been stolen; and the Greek princess and the two young men who were destined for the altar are even now rowing away in a boat which was awaiting them. But if the King will hasten, they may yet be caught; for at this moment they are battling with an adverse wind, and they have no knowledge of the currents of that treacherous shore.

Thoas, furious at the trap into which he has fallen, gives rapid orders: a company of herdsmen is to go to the headlands, and boats are to put off immediately from the shore. So these crafty Greeks will be overtaken, either by sea or land; and let them beware of a barbarian's anger! But suddenly, through the shouting and confusion, there is a roll of thunder and a lightning-flash; and descending through the air the goddess Athene is seen. Her voice rings out imperiously, commanding Thoas to stay his haste. Then, in the awed hush that falls, she makes known the will of the gods that Orestes and his sister shall not be pursued. Fate has ordained their escape, and Thoas may not strive against it; for Destiny has given to that fleeing priestess to end her days in peace and gentleness.

M. C. STURGEON, *Women of the Classics* (adapted)

THE ADVENTURES OF AENEAS

YOU have read how Aeneas escaped from the flames of Troy, carrying his aged father and leading his little son Iulus. He was joined by other refugees from the doomed city, and the story of their wandering in quest of a new home is told by the Latin poet Virgil in his great poem the *Aeneid*.

A RESCUE

AFTER many years of adventuring they see the shores of Italy, and far away, on the southern horizon, rises the fiery crest of Aetna. To the right they hear an angry, moaning sound, which warns them that they are on the threshold of the dread Sicilian strait, the abode of Scylla and Charybdis. Even at this distance the billows rise to a gigantic height, threatening to swamp their vessels. Palinurus, the captain of Aeneas' ship, calls to his men to take to their oars ; the rest of the fleet follow his example, and, borne forward by oars and sails, they are soon out of the reach of danger. With sunset the wind dropped, and after hours of weary toil they landed in the darkness beneath the black shadow of Aetna, where the giant Enceladus lies chained on his uneasy couch. For after the defeat of the Titans, the enormous brood of Earth, who had risen up in revolt against Jove, Enceladus, the most violent of these fierce rebels, was confined in a subterranean dungeon, and the huge mass of Aetna was flung upon his bruised limbs to keep him fast ; and whenever he stirs in that living grave the whole mountain quakes and trembles, and fire and smoke and molten rocks are belched up through the throat of the furnace.

Fevered was the sleep and troubled the dreams of the Trojans while their fleet lay moored in that fearful neighbourhood. The night was black and starless, and the air was full of strange sounds, as if some vast, primeval monster were groaning and gasping for breath. The day dawned red and threatening, and Aeneas had given the order to embark, when out of the woods which clothe the lower slopes of Aetna a man came slowly limping, whose appearance showed him to be in the last extremity of want and misery. He was covered with mire, and clothed in rags, scarce held together with thorns, and his face was almost hidden by a matted growth of hair and beard. In such guise he came on with feeble steps, holding out his hands like one imploring pity and protection. When he recognized the Trojan arms and dress he halted suddenly, and seemed to hesitate ; then, summoning resolution, he came on again with quickened steps, and flung himself at the knees of Aeneas, who had advanced to meet him.

" Save me," he cried, speaking in the Greek language, with sobs and tears ; " only take me from this horrible place, and then use me as ye will. I am a Greek, as ye hear, and I fought with the other Greeks against Troy. If that is a crime past forgiveness let me suffer for it ; tear me limb from limb, and fling the fragments on the waves—it will be something to be slaughtered by human hands."

Touched to the heart by that speaking image of wretchedness and despair, Aeneas raised the poor outcast from the ground, comforted him with gentle words, and encouraged him to tell his story. Reassured by this kind reception he informed them that he was one of the comrades of Ulysses, left behind in their hasty flight from the

K

cave of the Cyclops Polyphemus. For the hardy Ithacan had visited this island in his wanderings, and had put out the single eye of Polyphemus, which flamed like the sun in the centre of his forehead, in revenge for the murder of his comrades, whom the cannibal monster had slain and devoured. For three months the unhappy castaway had skulked in the woods, supporting life on berries and roots, and affrighted by the ponderous tread of Polyphemus and his brethren, and their mighty voices, which rumbled like thunder over his head. Then, catching sight of the Trojan vessels, he had crept from his hiding-place, determined to trust himself to the mercy of the newcomers, whoever they might be.

He had just finished his story when a sound of crashing boughs was heard, as if some great beast were advancing through the jungle ; and in a moment the giant shepherd came into view, supporting his footsteps on the trunk of a tall pine. Slowly he felt his way towards the sea, that monster horrible, misshapen, huge, and sightless ; and when he reached the margin of the bay he knelt down, and washed the oozing gore from the gaping pit in his brow, while groans, as of some wounded leviathan, made the very waters tremble.

In wild panic the people of Aeneas fled to their ships, and the hollow cliffs resounded to the beat of a thousand oars as they made haste to reach the open sea. Polyphemus heard, and waded out into deep water in the direction of the sound, with arms outstretched, to seize one of the flying vessels. But, finding himself outpaced, he lifted up his voice, and sent forth a colossal shout, which was bellowed back from the caverns of Aetna, and reached the far-off shores of Italy. Roused by that tremendous signal his brethren came rushing from the woods, and gathered in dread conclave, filling all the beach. Like towering oaks they stood or tall cypress-trees, glaring with orbs of fire at the Trojan fleet and the dashing oars. But the wind blew fair, and soon that tall cohort dwindled to pigmy size in the distance, and the rugged outlines of Aetna grew fainter and fainter.

H. L. HAVELL, *Stories from the Aeneid*

THE DEATH OF DIDO

[A STORM drove the voyagers into the harbour of Carthage on the north coast of Africa. There they were hospitably received by Queen Dido, a Phoenician refugee from Tyre who had fled from the evil rule of her brother to found a new city. The Queen fell in love with Aeneas, but in spite of her earnest entreaties to remain, the Trojan set sail to fulfil the commands of the gods. In despair at the desertion of her lover Dido took her own life.]

As soon as day comes, she begins with deliberate care to make all ready for her death. Under her directions, a great pyre is built within the courtyard, on which the Queen announces that she intends to offer a solemn sacrifice. Every relic of Aeneas is gathered and laid upon it ; his armour, his cloak, and his sword ; while all about it Dido herself hangs garlands and funeral chaplets. Her sister and her women wonder, but have no hint of her intention. When night falls and all the palace is sunk in sleep, Dido stands before the altar and consecrates herself for the sacrifice. But she cannot yet take the fatal step. She longs for one more look from her watch-tower, down upon the ships that are so soon to carry her lover away. So she strains her eyes through the darkness, only to find, with the first gleam of light, that the harbour is bare. The fleet has sailed : Aeneas, warned by a vision from Jove, has fled in the night. A bitter cry escapes her. She calls upon the great powers of Earth and Sky and the dreadful Underworld to avenge her wrongs ; and looking

forward to the years that are to come, she invokes upon
Aeneas and his descendants the curse that followed the
Roman race through many generations :

> " So then do you,
> My Tyrians, harry with envenomed hate
> His race and kin through ages yet to come :
> Be this your tribute to my timeless death ! . . .
> Let coast conflict with coast, and sea with sea,
> Embattled host with host, and endless war
> Be waged, 'twixt their and your posterity ! " [1]

Then, rushing to the courtyard, she climbs the great pyre,
and grasps Aeneas' sword, and falls upon it.

So died the founder of Carthage ; and the father of great
Rome, looking back with remorseful eyes from his fleeing
ship, saw the flames of her pyre reddening the dawn.

M. C. STURGEON, *Women of the Classics*

HERCULES AND CACUS

[THE Trojan fleet reached Italy, and Aeneas sought the
friendship and help of Evander of Pallanteum.]   The sun
had passed the zenith when they saw the rude towers and
scattered houses of that humble town on the site of which
afterwards stood, and stands even to this day, the Eternal
City.

It chanced on that day that Evander, with Pallas his
son, and the elders of the little city, was offering sacrifice
to Hercules in a shady meadow by the riverside.   When
they heard the plash of oars, and saw the tall prows
rounding a bend of the stream, they rose in alarm from
their seats, fearing the approach of an enemy ; and Pallas,
snatching up a weapon, took his stand on the high bank
of the river, and cried : " Who are ye that thus invade
our waters ?   Come ye in peace or in war ? "   " We come

[1] From Sir Theodore Martin's translation of the *Aeneid*.

in peace," answered Aeneas from his place on the lofty
stern of his vessel. "We are the sons of Troy, driven
by the arms of the Latins to seek your alliance." "You
are welcome, then," answered Pallas, "Come and speak
with my father Evander."

Being led into the presence of Evander, Aeneas explained his errand, and Evander gazed earnestly in his
face while he spoke, as one who recalls to memory the
features of a friend. "Thou art no stranger to me," he
answered; "thou hast the very form and features of
Anchises, who came to the house of my father as one of
the train of royal Priam. And he gave me gifts at parting—
a quiver of Lycian arrows and a mantle embroidered in
gold and two gold pieces—which my son Pallas still has.
Therefore right welcome to my roof, and, as an earnest of
our friendship, come and take part in this annual feast to
Hercules."

With these kind words of welcome he conducted
Aeneas to a place of honour, and seated him on a chair of
maple wood covered with a shaggy lion's hide. Then the
banquet was resumed, and the guests were feasted on the
choicest portions of the meat, and cheered with cups of
generous wine.

When their hunger was appeased and the bowls had
been replenished, Evander turned to his guest, and said:
"Think not that this is an empty rite, born of super-
stition, which ever runs after new gods and new forms of
worship, forsaking the old; no, my friend, it is a debt of
deep gratitude which we are paying, in memory of our
salvation from dreadful peril. Look yonder at that
shattered peak; see how its sides have been rent and
torn, and mark the shivered rocks which strew its base.
That seat of desolation was once the home of Cacus, a
monster, half man, half brute, who dwelt in a deep,
sunless cave, whose floor ran continually with human

blood, while the ghastly heads of his victims, smeared with gore, were hung as trophies at his doors. The father of this cannibal giant was Vulcan, and from Vulcan came the fiery blast which poured in smoke and flames from his cavernous maw.

"Long we prayed for help against this scourge of our land, and at last our prayer was answered. For Hercules, after the slaughter of Geryon, passed this way, driving before him the oxen which he had won as the spoils of that victory, and rested in this valley to feed and water his herd. And while he slept in the shadow of the trees Cacus, who lusted after the flesh of the fat beeves, stole four bulls, and as many heifers, the finest of the herd, and hid them in his cave, dragging them backward by their tails, so as to disguise their tracks, and make it seem that they had gone the other way. When Hercules awoke he sought in vain for the stolen cattle, and prepared to leave the valley with what remained of the beasts. Missing their companions the steers bellowed loud and long as they moved away, and an answering bellow came from the depth of the cavern where Cacus had concealed his plunder.

"Dire was the rage of Hercules when he heard that signal, and, guided by the sound, he rushed up the path which led to the cave, brandishing his huge club of knotted oak. Cacus, when he saw him coming, let fall a massive block of stone, which was suspended by chains over the entrance, and just as Hercules arrived, panting and furious, the weighty portcullis dropped into its place, barring the way. In vain Hercules flung himself against that stony barrier; even he could not stir it a hair's breadth.

"There was a tall crag, rising like a pointed spire above the rocky mass which defended the home of Cacus, and a favourite haunt and nesting-place of ravens. Hercules selected this as his point of attack, and, climbing to the roof of the cavern, leaned against the rude column with all his weight, gripping it in his mighty arms ; then, after one final heave, he let go, and the vast granite pillar, torn from its foundations, toppled and fell, like an avalanche of stone, damming the stream below, and leaving a black, yawning chasm, like the mouth of some great furnace when the fires are out. For a moment Hercules stood peering into that infernal pit, which reminded him of the day when he went down into the Underworld to fetch the three-headed hound of Pluto, and the pale ghosts fled affrighted from his club and his bow. Far beneath he caught sight of the cowering form of Cacus, who was now howling with terror ; and first he assailed the shrinking monster with a shower of rocks, big as millstones, and broken boughs. Driven to extremity Cacus vomited forth a volume of smoke and flame, which filled all the cavern, and poured its choking fumes through the opening above. The undaunted hero, whose foe was thus hidden from view, flung himself into that whirlpool of flame and smoke, and, reaching the bottom, fastened his iron fingers on the throat of Cacus, and strangled him slowly to death.

" Then for the first time we saw the guilty secrets of that cannibal den. The gates of stone were torn from their sockets, the stolen cattle were released, and the hideous corpse of Cacus was dragged forth by the heels. Like some vast dragon he lay, now limp and lifeless, with eyes staring ghastly, and gaping mouth, from which smoke was still oozing.

" Not without reason, therefore, have we built this high altar and instituted this annual feast to the memory of Hercules. And ye too, our kinsmen, should join with all your hearts in the worship of the hero to whom we owe so much."

H. L. HAVELL, *Stories from the Aeneid*

THE SHIELD OF AENEAS

VENUS was filled with alarm for her son when she saw the formidable coalition which Turnus, Prince of the Rutulians, was gathering against him, and remembering that Vulcan had forged a suit of invulnerable armour for Achilles, she determined to ask the same service for Aeneas. Arming herself with all her blandishments she thus preferred her plea to the rugged fire god : " Lord of my love, thou seest what perils are menacing my Trojan hero. As long as the Greeks were fighting against Troy I never asked thy aid. But now he has come by divine command to the fields of Italy, and in serving him thou art serving our common sovereign, Jove. I beseech thee, therefore, refuse not to me the boon which thou didst grant to Thetis and to Memnon's mother. Let my champion go to battle sheathed in armour of thy making, and armed with a spear of ethereal temper, like theirs."

The good-natured god readily granted his fair wife's request, and in the chilly hour before dawn, when thrifty housewives leave their warm beds to begin the toils of the day, he entered his subterranean smithy, whose chimney is the towering peak of Aetna. There toils the divine smith, with his helpers the giant Cyclopes, and the fire and smoke of their furnace are belched from Aetna's black throat, and all the land heaves and quakes to the shock of their anvils. He found his brawny mates already hard at work shaping a thunderbolt for the armoury of Jove with terror and with tempest and with fire. Others were fashioning a new chariot for Mars ; and one grim giant was busy polishing the dread aegis, the shield of Minerva, where serpents of living gold writhe and hiss, and glares the Gorgon's head, the neck severed, the eyes rolling. " Put all this aside," said the master, entering the forge. " To-day I have other work for you to do.

Arms are to be made for a warrior." Forthwith the whole company apply themselves to this new task; some work the huge bellows, and send the red flames leaping and roaring to the cavern's roof; some temper the white, hissing blade in water. The molten bronze bubbles in the crucibles and the deadly steel turns from white to red as it takes shape on the anvil.

And what words can tell of all the wonder of the shield and the pictured history wrought on its surface by the fire god? Here Aeneas saw displayed all the deeds of his posterity and all the tale of Rome. There was seen Romulus and his twin brother nursed by the grim she-wolf; here was pictured the rape of the Sabine women, with the war which followed, and the treaty which united the three races. Not far from these stood the haughty Porsena, bringing back Tarquin, the tyrant; and Horatius keeping the bridge single-handed against an army. Here towered the citadel on the Capitoline Hill, and the Gauls were seen creeping through the bushes to the assault; but the sacred geese gave signal of their approach, and Manlius called the garrison to arms.

Bordering each pictured panel, ran the broad waters of the sea, its waves fashioned in gold, with silver foam, and in the centre a wide space was left, on which was portrayed the famous sea-fight of Actium. On one side were the light galleys of the Romans, led by Augustus and the faithful Agrippa; on the other side loomed the gigantic hulls of Antonius, swarming with all the hordes of the corrupt and barbarous East, and in their centre, O shame to tell! were seen the silken sails of the gilded vessel in which sat Cleopatra, his Egyptian spouse. Above the helm of Augustus beamed a bright star, the happy star of Julius, and all the guardian spirits of Rome were arrayed on his side. On the cliffs of Leucate stood an armed multitude watching the fray. And now they rush to battle, and all the sea is churned into foam ; like islands torn from their foundations, or mountains afloat, the huge galleons of Egypt sweep down upon the Roman fleet. Long and deadly is the conflict ; but at length fire begins to break out among the ships of Antonius, and Cleopatra gives the signal for retreat. The mourning Nile receives the fugitives into his bosom, and there the guilty queen and the lover whom she had betrayed find their doom.

Last of all, to close this eventful history, was seen the triumph of Augustus after his victory. It was a day of solemn festival in Rome, and all the streets were thronged by the joyful people ; every altar smoked, and every temple was filled with songs of thanksgiving. A long procession of captives passed before the gazing multitude. Of every nation and of every language were they : the swarthy African, and the Arab in his flowing gown, the yellow Tartar, the Celt, and the Teuton. For on that day all peoples owned one yoke, from the wild waters of Araxes to the Atlantic waves.

H. L. HAVELL, *Stories from the Aeneid*

CAMILLA

AMONG those who fought against the Trojans in Italy was Camilla, a warlike maiden, whose hands had never known the touch of spindle or distaff, but wielded spear and sword. Light of foot was she, and swift as the winds of heaven, so that she could tread the heaving waters without wetting her feet, or fly like a bird over a field of growing corn. Many an eye would follow the proud warrior maid as she marshalled her troop, spear in hand, clothed in a crimson tunic, with brooch of gold, and bearing a well-filled quiver on her shoulders. . . .

She was the daughter of a Volscian chieftain named Metabus, who was driven by sedition, while she was still an infant, from his native city. Hotly pursued by his enemies, and carrying the little babe in his arms, Metabus sought an asylum in the depths of the forest. But before he had reached a place of safety his path was crossed by a roaring mountain torrent. To cross those boiling waters with that tender burden in his arms was impossible, and in every other direction the woods were swarming with his foes. For a while he stood irresolute, gazing on the yellow, leaping waves, then at last came to a desperate resolve. In his right hand he was carrying a weighty spear ; to this he bound the child, first wrapping her in a thick envelope of bark torn from the neighbouring trees ; then he poised the weapon, with its precious load, in his sinewy hand, and called aloud to Diana : " Daughter of Latona, guard and preserve my child, and she shall be thine, and serve thee all her days." His prayer ended he brandished, he flung the spear ; the torrent roared, like a wild beast cheated of his prey ; and at the same moment a loud shout was heard, and the foremost of the pursuers rushed upon Metabus. In he plunged, and after a tough struggle reached the farther shore, where he found the weapon buried deep in the bank, and his daughter, still wrapped in her strange swaddling clothes, safe and unharmed.

Faithful to his vow he bred Camilla as a servant of the virgin goddess, who loves the hunter's cry, and the wild, free life of the woods and mountains. With his own hand he nursed her on the milk of mares, and as soon as she could walk alone he trained her to use the bow and spear, and instructed her in all the woodman's lore. Clad in a short tunic of tiger-skin she passed her days in the chase by her father's side, and at night she slept under the open sky. So she grew up in matchless beauty and strength, swift of foot, and sure of hand, with a soul white and cold as the snow.　H. L. HAVELL, *Stories from the Aeneid*

FROM THE HISTORIANS

CROESUS, KING OF LYDIA

THROUGH the fair plains of Lydia flows the golden stream of the Pactolus. And concerning this river a wondrous tale is told. Midas, King of Phrygia, had pleased the mighty god Bacchus, and the god, in gratitude, bade him ask a gift. Then Midas uttered this foolish prayer : " Grant, great Bacchus, that whatever I touch may turn to gold." Bacchus was grieved at his folly ; but, bound by his promise, and wishing Midas to learn a lesson, he granted his desire. So Midas, to prove the god, picked up a stone, and lo ! the stone was solid gold. Then he took off his sandals, and trod the ground with his bare feet, and wherever he stepped he left a footprint of pure gold. And so he went on, wild with joy, turning everything within his reach to gold. But his joy was short-lived. Soon he grew hungry, and sat down to meat, but the first morsel which touched his lips stiffened into gold. He was thirsty, and raised the cup to his lips ; in a moment his mouth was filled with golden mud. Then all at once the magnitude of the curse which he had brought upon himself came home to him. Master of boundless wealth, he was poorer than the poorest slave in his house. He was starving in the midst of millions ! In dire distress, he turned again to the god, and begged him to take back his gift. And Bacchus had pity, and answered : " Poor fool ! thou wouldst be rich, and now thou art poor indeed. But if thou hast learnt thy lesson I will plague thee no more ; after short penance

the curse shall be removed. Hear now my command : go
thou to the Pactolus, and enter the stream, and wade breast-
deep in the water up to the river's source ; there plunge
thy head in the spouting waters as they gush upward
from their fount, and wash clean thy body, and wash away
thy guilt." The wondering Midas faltered his thanks, and
did as he was bade. And as he staggered upward, stem-
ming the rushing stream, the golden gift passed from his
body into the waters ; and from that hour the Pactolus
brought wealth on his flood, and all his sands were gold.

On his banks rose the great city of Sardis, where the
kings of Lydia built their palace, and held their court.
The most famous of these was Croesus, whose story we
are to hear. He was the richest man of his time, and his
name is still a proverb for boundless wealth. Not content
with his own great kingdom, he conquered the Greeks
who had built cities on his coast ; but having conquered
them he ruled them, not as a tyrant, but as a father and
lord. Thus Sardis grew famous and mighty, and the
name of Croesus spread far and wide, and wise men came
from distant lands to see him, and wonder at his state.

Wisest of all these was Solon of Athens, who had made
good laws for the men of his city, and saved them from
misery and ruin. But, fearing that if he remained in
Athens he would be compelled to change some of his laws,
he went away for ten years, first binding the Athenians
by a solemn oath not to change anything until his return.
During these ten years he visited many strange countries,
and while still on his travels he came to Lydia. Croesus,
who had heard of his wisdom and his renown, welcomed
him, and feasted him in the palace, and showed him all
the glory and wealth of Sardis. One evening, as they
were sitting together after a gorgeous banquet, Croesus
turned to Solon, and said : " My friend, we have heard
much of thy wisdom and thy travels—how that thou

roamest over the whole earth in search of knowledge—now, therefore, we would fain ask thee a question : Who is he whom thou callest the happiest of men ? " So Croesus inquired of Solon, tempting him, and expecting him to answer : " Croesus the Lydian." But Solon was no flatterer, so he answered, in all honesty : " Tellus the Athenian." Croesus, who had never heard of Tellus, asked who he was, and why Solon called him the happiest of men. And Solon replied : " Tellus lived at Athens in the days of her prosperity, and lived to see his children's children happy and thriving ; and being rich, as we in Athens count riches, he died a noble death : for he routed the foes of his native city in battle, and died in the hour of victory ; and the Athenians buried him at the public cost, and remember his name with honour and love." Then for some minutes there was silence, while Croesus pondered on the words of Solon. But, thinking that he would win at least the second place, he asked who was second in happiness to Tellus. Solon answered : " Cleobis and Biton of Argos. They had enough of this world's goods, and were mighty athletes. Their home was in the country, eight miles from the city, where stands the temple of the great goddess Hera. Now it happened, when the yearly festival of Hera came round, and their mother wished to visit the temple, that the oxen who should have drawn her carriage were working in the fields some way from the house. There was no time to fetch the oxen, so these strong and pious youths themselves put on the yoke, and drew their mother in the heavy car all those eight weary miles to the town. Great was the wonder of the multitude thronging the streets as the strange procession passed by—the gallant lads straining at the yoke, and the car with its precious burden creaking and rumbling behind. The mother's eyes were moist with happy tears as she heard the shouts of the great host of worshippers, who stood wondering at the manly beauty of her sons, while the women cried out blessings on their stout and loving hearts. Then she alighted, and went up into the temple to pray. And she fell on her knees in the awful presence of the goddess, and cried: 'Grant, O goddess, to my sons, who have honoured me thus, that gift which is the best of all gifts for man.' Her prayer was answered; for when the young men had offered sacrifice and taken their share in the feast they lay down in the temple to sleep, and in the morning they were found in the same place, sleeping the long and quiet sleep of death." Then Croesus was wroth, and spake: "Art thou then blind, Solon, that, after thine eyes have looked on all my glory and my state, thou holdest me of less account than these men of naught, these common drudges of Athens and Argos?" Solon replied: "Croesus, thou hast asked me concerning the lot of man. Now I know that the gods are full of envy, and look on human happiness with grudging eyes. The days of the years of our life are threescore years and ten, or, if a man be very strong, perhaps fourscore. And in all the many thousand days of those seventy or eighty years how many fickle chances, how many envious blows of Fate, have we not to face! Think not that all the glitter of thy gold, nor all thy pomp and power, can save thee from Fortune's wanton whim. Too often the sunny day of happiness ends in the black night of misery and disaster. Therefore I say that we may call no man happy until he is dead." But Solon's words seemed to Croesus as the words of folly, and he dismissed the sage in anger and contempt.

[Croesus' son died] and for two years the father mourned for his son. Then matters of greater import, and the peril threatening from the East, turned his thoughts from private grief to public care. For meanwhile great things had been happening in Asia. The Persians, under Cyrus, had risen against their masters, the Medes, and overthrown their empire, and now ruled over all those vast regions which the Medes in their day had wrested from the Assyrians. As he watched the growth of this new power Croesus began to tremble for his own kingdom, and thought it was wise to check the tide of invasion before it overflowed his own borders. But, wishing first to learn the will of Heaven, he sent messengers to consult the oracle of Delphi. There were many oracles in the ancient world, but the most famous of all was that of the Delphian Apollo. At the foot of Mount Parnassus, in Central Greece, there is a deep cavern, and in the midst of the cavern there is a rent in the rock running down deep into the recesses of the earth. Here sat the Sibyl, or priestess, and listened to the divine voice which was borne upward from the mysterious Underworld. Sitting thus on her sacred seat, called a tripod, and breathing the heavy vapours which poured out of the chasm, she became filled with a sort of frenzy, and uttered words of dark and awful import. These were written down by the priest, generally in verse, and handed to those who came to learn the will of the god. Before the cavern was a splendid temple to the Delphian Apollo, rich with the costly offerings of the many great and mighty men who had used the oracle.

Croesus resolved to consult the Delphic god and sent his messengers with many costly gifts to ask if the god advised him to march against the Persians. Then came the answer : " *If Croesus crosses the Halys a mighty kingdom shall fall.*" Great was the joy of Croesus ; for he did not see that the oracle was of the two-edged kind, which cuts both ways ; and he thought that the " mighty kingdom " mentioned was that of Persia. So he made ready his army, and marched against Cyrus. He crossed the Halys, which was then the boundary between the Lydian and Persian dominions, and met the army of Cyrus in the country called Cappadocia. Here a fierce battle was fought, in which neither side gained the mastery. Next day Croesus, seeing that the Persians made no movement against him, and thinking that his forces were too small to strike a decisive blow, marched back to Sardis, and disbanded his army, intending to assemble a great force, and renew the struggle next year. Then a strange thing occurred : all the pastures about Sardis where the horses fed were filled with serpents ; and the horses left eating the grass, and began to devour the serpents. The wise men whom Croesus consulted interpreted the event thus : " The serpent," they said, " is a child of the soil, the horse a foreigner and a foe, and the devouring of the serpents by the horses is a sign that a foreign host is coming to destroy the native children of Lydia."

Cyrus was not the man to neglect such an opportunity. When he learnt that Croesus had sent away his army he marched straight into Lydia, and encamped under the walls of Sardis. Croesus, thus driven to extremity, led out such forces as he had left, and gave battle in the plain before the city. Now, the Lydians were famous horsemen, and though in after days they became soft and cowardly, at this time there were no braver or stouter warriors than they. But a cunning Mede had advised Cyrus how he might make the cavalry of Croesus useless. There were many camels following the Persian army, laden with stores and provisions. Cyrus caused their burdens to be removed, and mounted on each camel a Persian soldier, armed as a horseman. Thus equipped, the camels were drawn up in the van of the Persian army ; behind them followed the infantry, and after them the cavalry. Now, the sight and smell of a camel is odious

L

to a horse, and when the horses in the Lydian army saw
the camels, and scented them as they came on with the
wind, they grew restive, shied, and, soon breaking away
from all control, threw the Lydian army into confusion.
Still, the Lydians did not give way, but, dismounting
from their horses, fought where they stood, and slew
many of the Persians. At last the Persians gained the
upper hand ; the Lydians fled with Croesus into their
citadel, and Cyrus laid siege to the place. Forty days the
siege lasted, and then Cyrus, growing weary, offered great
rewards to the man who should be first to mount the wall.

There was one steep and perilous path, leading up the
most precipitous part of the cliff, and one day a Persian
soldier saw one of the Lydian garrison descending by this
way to pick up his helmet, which had dropped from the wall.
Having marked the way, he scaled the cliff, with several
of his comrades ; for the Persians were homebred mountaineers. The garrison was surprised ; the Persians poured
in, cut the defenders to pieces, and sacked the citadel.

Cyrus had given strict orders to spare the life of Croesus
and bring him safe into his presence. And it so happened
that a son of Croesus who had caused his father much
sorrow by his dumbness was now the means of saving him
from a violent death. Croesus had tried all means to cure
him of his infirmity, and inquiring once at Delphi on his
behalf had received this answer :

> "Son of Lydia, mighty Croesus, small of wit, though great
>   in power,
> Since thy happy days are numbered, hasten not the woeful
>   hour :
> When the voice for which thou longest rings within thy
>   palace hall,
> In that self-same hour thy kingdom bows and totters to her
>   fall."

The moment for the fulfilment of the oracle had now

arrived. For a Persian soldier, not knowing Croesus, was rushing on him to slay him, and Croesus, overwhelmed by his misfortunes, prepared sullenly to receive the stroke. The horror of that sight loosened the boy's tongue, and he cried : " Fellow, slay not Croesus ! " Thus in the hour of his father's disaster speech was given to the son, and he retained the gift till the end of his life.

Perhaps the Persian had made a vow to sacrifice Croesus ; perhaps he wished to make trial of the gods whether they would save him who had worshipped and honoured them so long. He had commanded a great pile of wood to be raised, and Croesus was set bound on the top, with twice seven of the sons of Lydia. Suddenly, as Croesus stood, bound with chains and waiting for the fire, the words of Solon, long forgotten, came back to his memory : " Call no man happy till he is dead." Roused from his stupor, he lifted up his head, and cried thrice, in a loud and lamentable voice : " Solon ! Solon ! Solon ! " Cyrus commanded his interpreters to ask who Solon was, and why Croesus called thus on his name. At first Croesus would not answer, but being pressed, he said : " I would that all the tyrants might hear the words of that same Solon." Questioned further, at last he told all the tale, conveying that solemn warning to all who build their hopes on outward pomp and state. And the stern heart of the conqueror was touched, and something of fear crept in besides when he thought that he too was mortal, and that this Croesus, whom he had doomed to a cruel death, was not long ago as great as himself. In this altered mood he gave orders to quench the fire, which was now burning fiercely. But when they tried, they could not master the flames. When Croesus saw them vainly trying to quench the burning pile he understood that Cyrus had repented. Then desire of life came back strongly upon him, and he lifted up his voice, and called to Apollo, beseeching the god to remember his services and come to his aid. And suddenly the sky was overcast the sun was hidden in black clouds, a violent storm of rain descended, and the flames were quenched.

Thus Croesus was saved, and Cyrus set him on a throne next to himself, and ever after held him in high esteem. Croesus outlived his conqueror, and remained an honoured guest in the Court of Persia until his end.

H. L. HAVELL, *Stories from Herodotus*

MARATHON

The mountains look on Marathon—
   And Marathon looks on the sea ;
And musing there an hour alone,
   I dream'd that Greece might still be free ;
For standing on the Persians' grave,
I could not deem myself a slave.[1]

[DARIUS, the King of the Persians, whose vast empire included modern Persia, Baluchistan, Afghanistan, Egypt Syria, and Asia Minor, determined to make his power felt in Greece. In 492 B.C. he dispatched a great fleet which was destroyed by a violent storm off the promontory of Mount Athos. Before making another attempt to attack the Greeks he sent envoys to all the states, demanding earth and water, the usual tokens of submission. The men of Athens, it is said, dropped the King's envoys into a chasm to find earth for themselves, while the Spartans dropped the envoys into a deep well to search for water. Then, in 490 B.C., Darius sent his army by sea straight across the Aegean from Asia Minor. His men landed north-east of Athens, on the wide, level bay of Marathon, which was backed by the mountains and bordered on each side by a stream.]

[1] From Byron's *The Isles of Greece*.

When the news of the landing reached Athens, the Athenians set out in full force to meet the invaders. They were led by ten generals, among whom was Miltiades. Before they left the city the generals sent off Pheidippides, a swift runner, and courier by profession, with an urgent message to Sparta. It was a long and difficult journey : his road lay from Athens to Eleusis ; then on through the Isthmus by Megara and Corinth ; over the borders of Sicyon and Argos into the wild mountains of Arcadia ; and so by a steep descent into the vale of Sparta. Yet such was his speed and endurance that he reached Sparta the day after leaving Athens. He was nearing the end of his journey, crossing Mount Parthenius, when he heard a voice calling : " Pheidippides ! Pheidippides ! " He paused, full of fear, for he knew that it was no mortal speech which was wakening the echoes on that wild mountain's side. Then he heard a rustling in the wood hard by, the boughs swayed, and parted, and before him stood the great god Pan. " Fear not, Pheidippides," said the god ; " I am thy friend, and the friend of them that sent thee ; and I would know why they at Athens pay me neither worship nor regard, who have served them before, and would serve them again. While, as for thee,

> " For what thou hast done
> Count on a worthy reward ! Henceforth be allowed
>   thee release
> From the racer's toil, no vulgar reward in praise or
>   in pelf ! " [1]

Saying this, the vision was gone. On his return to Athens, Pheidippides duly reported what he had seen and heard ; and the Athenians, as soon as their affairs allowed it,

[1] From Browning's *Pheidippides*. The interpolation of these lines is the present editor's.

built a temple to Pan, and honoured him with a yearly
sacrifice and torch-race.

But at present his first concern was with the Spartans
so on he sped, his mind full of the god, scaled the last
steep ascent, and shot like an arrow down the mountain
path into the valley of the Eurotas. Breathless and
travel-stained, he stood before the magistrates, and
panted out his message : " Spartans, the Athenians beg
you to aid them, and not to suffer the most ancient city in
Greece to fall under the yoke of barbarians. Already
Eretria has fallen, and Greece is poorer by one city of
no mean note." Now, the Spartans were willing to help
the Athenians, but they were held back by a religious
scruple : that month was sacred to Apollo, and before the
full moon it was not lawful for them to leave the city.

It looked, therefore, as if the Athenians would have to
bear the brunt alone ; but while they were standing in
order of battle, on a spot sacred to Hercules, overlooking
the bay of Marathon, a gallant little band came trooping
down the mountain-side, and joined their ranks. It was
the whole military force of Plataea, a little town on the
borders of Attica and Boeotia, between which and Athens
there was an old tie of friendship and alliance. Thus
reinforced the generals held a council of war. Their
opinion was divided : five were for giving battle to the
Persians without delay, and among these was Miltiades
five were against it. Then Miltiades went to Callimachus,
who by virtue of his office as polemarch voted as eleventh
man with the generals, and whose decision was, therefore
all-important, and entreated him very earnestly, saying
" Callimachus, the fate of the Athenians is in thy hands
speak the word only : is she to be free or enslaved ? Now
mayest thou win thee a name. If we fight and win to-day,
Athens shall be greatest among the cities of Greece. If
we do not fight, there are traitors among us who are

watching an occasion to betray us to the Persians. Vote, then, as one on whose voice the fate of Athens, the fate of Greece, depends." Happily for Athens, happily for mankind, the words of Miltiades prevailed. Callimachus gave his vote for battle.

Some days passed ; at length, on the day when the chief command came round to Miltiades (for each of the ten generals held it in turn), he drew up his army for the fight. On the right wing Callimachus was in command ; the left was occupied by the Plataeans. To prevent the risk of outflanking, the chief strength was thrown into the wings, and the centre was consequently weakened. Then there was a pause : on the slope of the hill stood that devoted little band ; on the plain below were arrayed the cavalry, the archers, and the infantry of Persia, outnumbering them by ten to one. In front of the Greeks stands the priest ; the victims are brought, the sacrifice is declared favourable, and the voice of the people is lifted up in prayer. Then the trumpet sounds, and loud and clear rings out the order : " Charge ! " Beneath the tramp of ten thousand feet the hillside thunders and trembles ; with a mighty shout the army of Athens sweeps down like a torrent on the plain below. A space of nearly a mile had to be passed before they could come to blows with the enemy ; the Persians, therefore, had ample time to make their reflections, as that living flood of warriors poured on, with flash of shields and glitter of spears. " Madmen ! They are rushing into the jaws of death ! " —such was the proud thought of the conquerors of Asia. But they were soon undeceived : in a moment the Athenians were upon them, and down went horse and foot, bowman and slinger. On the wings the Athenians and Plataeans at once bore down all resistance, and hurled the Persians opposed to them back upon the sea ; then, facing round, they went to the support of their own centre, which, borne back by the weight and mass of the enemy, had retired inland. Here too they were victorious ; and now the rout became general, and the whole Persian army was flying in wild disorder towards their ships.

H. L. HAVELL, *Stories from Herodotus*

So, when Persia was dust, all cried, " To Akropolis !
Run, Pheidippides, one race more ! the meed is thy
    due !
' Athens is saved, thank Pan,' go shout ! " He flung
    down his shield,
Ran like fire once more : and the space 'twixt the
    Fennel-field
And Athens was stubble again, a field which a fire
    runs through,
Till in he broke : " Rejoice, we conquer ! " Like
    wine through clay,
Joy in his blood bursting his heart, he died.

ROBERT BROWNING, *Pheidippides*

THERMOPYLAE

THE news of the defeat of Marathon only added fuel to the wrath of Darius. Without losing a moment, he sent round orders to every province in his vast empire to make ready for another expedition, on a much grander scale than the last. Thereupon all Asia was in a bustle and ferment of preparation for the next three years. But the career of the lord of Asia was now drawing to its close. In the midst of his schemes of conquest and vengeance he sickened and died, five years after Marathon, and Xerxes, his son, succeeded him on the throne. The new monarch viewed with disfavour the intended war against Greece, and it needed all the arts of his courtiers to persuade him to carry out his father's plans.

During four years from the death of Darius the work of preparation went on. Not the least part of it was the cutting of a canal through the isthmus which joins the peninsula of Athos to the mainland. Already a Persian fleet, sent three years before Marathon against Greece, had been wrecked off that stormy headland; and this is why it was determined to cut through the isthmus, in order to avoid the dangerous passage round the cape. A great host was set to work, and they began to dig, with overseers standing over them, to assist their labours with the lash. As the trench grew deeper scaffolds were erected, tier above tier, on which stood men to hand up the soil in baskets as it was dug out. Now, most of the diggers were foolish, for they made the sides of the trench perpendicular, so that when it grew deep they were constantly delayed by the soil falling in. But the Phoenicians had the wit, when they began digging, to make the trench in the part allotted to them double the width required, gradually narrowing it as they proceeded; thus the sides were sloping and did not fall in. Three years were occupied in this task, and the canal was made broad enough for three triremes to row abreast. Stores of provisions were brought, and laid up at convenient spots on the line of march.

Meanwhile another great work was in progress—the bridging of the Hellespont. Beginning from Abydos, on the Asiatic shore, the Phoenicians and Egyptians, to whom this task was assigned, threw two bridges, joined with cables, across the strait to a point between Sestos and Madytus. The distance is nearly a mile. The work was hardly finished when a violent storm arose, and scattered the whole fabric. Perhaps the sea-god was angry at the yoke thus laid upon him—but not more angry than Xerxes when he heard of it. He fell into a fit of truly childish fury, and sent orders to flog the Hellespont with three hundred lashes, and sink a set of fetters into his waters. And those who flogged the waves were ordered to utter these words as they laid on the lash : " O bitter water, my master punishes thee thus, because thou hast wronged him, having suffered no wrong at his hands ; and Xerxes the king will pass over thee, whether thou wilt have it or not. No man offers sacrifice to thee ; and rightly so, thou treacherous and briny river." Having thus vented his rage on the river, he next gave orders to cut off the heads of the master-builders who had designed the bridges. Others were at once appointed to this dangerous office, and with such a warning before them, they were not likely to be careless of their work. Two lines of galleys—three hundred and sixty for the eastern bridge, and three hundred and fourteen for the other—were moored by huge anchors lengthways to the current. Across these great cables were stretched, six to each line of vessels, and drawn taut by capstans on either shore. Each yard of cable weighed a hundredweight. Then beams of wood were laid in order on the cables, and firmly fastened from above ; on the beams brushwood was piled, and over the brushwood was laid a layer of earth, firmly trodden in. On either side rose a high bulwark, lest the horses and baggage-mules should take fright at the sight of the sea.

All was now ready for an advance on Greece, and Xerxes set out with his host from Sardis at the beginning of the spring, and marched towards Abydos.

At the command of Xerxes a throne of white marble had been raised in a position affording a view over the surrounding country.

The King climbed the ascent, and sat down on the throne. He cast his eyes around, and saw beneath him the two wondrous bridges, and the waters of the Hellespont swarming with ships, and heard the air filled with the shouts of the busy multitude. Then he turned his gaze shoreward, and all the shore, as far as his eye could reach, was black with the countless host. And his heart swelled with joy and pride, as he thought that all this mighty armament called him lord.

Dawn is just breaking over the waters of the Hellespont, and the whole host of Persia is waiting in awed silence for the coming of the god of day. On the bridges many hands are busy, burning offerings of incense, and strewing the way with myrtle boughs. As the first rays shoot across the waters Xerxes takes a golden bowl, and, pouring drink-offerings into the sea, lifts up his voice in prayer. " God of my fathers," he cries, " let naught arise to stay my path until I have set foot as a conqueror on the farthest verge of Europe." Thus having said, he flung the cup into the sea, and after it a golden mixing-bowl and a Persian scimitar. Whether these were offerings to the sun, or gifts of atonement to the Hellespont, we cannot say. Sacrifice and prayer ended, the great passage of the Hellespont began. The infantry and cavalry crossed by the eastern bridge, the baggage-train by the western. Seven days and seven nights that living stream poured unceasingly from Asia into Europe. The names alone of the nations who made up the motley host would fill a page of this book—Medes and Persians, Assyrians and Chaldeans, Indians and Parthians, Egyptians, Arabians, and Ethiopians, and a hundred more. Almost every known race of mankind, and every degree of civilization and savagery, were represented there, from the gallant nobles of Persia, second to none in valour and warlike skill, to the rude natives of the Upper Nile, clothed in lion and panther skins, and armed with clubs and stone-headed arrows, who daubed their bodies, when they went into battle, with chalk and red ochre—such was the word of power which had called up these and other wild denizens from the uttermost parts of the earth.

At length the whole army passed over in safety, and by way of Thrace and Macedonia entered Greek territory. On this march Xerxes, it is said, brought more than one city to the brink of ruin by graciously consenting to dine at its expense. The cost of one such meal was ninety-six thousand pounds sterling of our money. Preparations were made months before ; vast stores of meal were laid up, with fat cattle, and poultry in thousands, and costly delicacies, and rare wines. A splendid pavilion was erected for the use of Xerxes and his courtiers, with vessels of silver and gold. When the feast was over the attendants of the King pulled up the tent-poles, and carried off the tent, furniture, gold and silver vessels, and all. A certain wit of Abdera, one of the cities which entertained these terrible guests, advised his fellow-citizens to go in a body to the temples, and give thanks to the gods that Xerxes did not dine twice in a day. " Two such dinners," he said, " and there would be nothing left for us to eat."

There is a wild and lonely spot, just opposite the northern point of Euboea, where the eastern spurs of the great mountain mass of Oeta leave a narrow strip of level land between themselves and the sea. Its name is Thermopylae—that is, the Hot Springs—and it is the ordinary entrance from Thessaly into Southern Greece. Here the Greeks resolved to make their first stand, and a force of three hundred Spartans, under Leonidas, their King, with a mixed body of other troops, numbering, in all, about five thousand, was sent to defend the pass.

When Xerxes, who was now encamped but a little way off, heard that a force of Spartans was waiting to oppose him at Thermopylae, he sent a horseman to see how many the Spartans were, and what they were doing. When the horseman rode up he found the entrance defended by a wall, so that he could not see those who were inside the pass; but outside the wall he saw a troop of Spartans, who were taking their turn at outpost duty, and some of them were at their exercises, while others were combing their long hair. They took not the least notice of him, so when he had gazed his fill he rode back, and told what he had seen.

On hearing his report Xerxes was sorely puzzled, not knowing what to make of it. He called Demaratus, the exiled King of Sparta, and asked what it meant; and Demaratus answered: " I have told thee before, O King, what manner of men the Spartans are; and now I tell thee again. These men have come to defend the pass against us; and it is their custom when about to run into peril of their lives to dress their heads. And know this, O King, that if thou canst conquer these men, and those who are left in Sparta, there will be none left to raise a hand against thee; for in Sparta is the noblest of monarchies, and the noblest of men are the Spartans." But his words seemed to Xerxes as idle tales, and he would not believe them. Four days he waited, expecting that the Greeks would run away; and on the fifth day, finding them still there, and thinking that they remained in sheer folly and wanton insolence, he sent some of his choicest troops, with orders to take them alive, and bring them into his presence. And these, being Medes and Cissians, charged down upon the Greeks. Many of them were slain; but others took their places, and a stubborn fight was kept up all day. Then it was made plain to the King that many are soldiers but few are men. When these were beaten off the King ordered the very flower of his army, the Immortals, to take up the task. These fared no better than the Medes; for in the narrow space they had no advantage from their numbers, and the spears which they used were shorter than those of the Greeks. The military habits and lifelong drill of the Spartans now stood them in good stead ; they fought with the Persians like seasoned veterans against raw recruits ; and sometimes they would feign flight, tempting the barbarians to pursue them—then, as the barbarians came on with wild cries and uproar, they wheeled round, and cut them down by hundreds. Again and again the Persians returned to the assault ; again and again they were hurled back with heavy loss. Xerxes, who sat watching the struggle, was seen to leap three times from his throne, in fear for his army. Next day the Persians, supposing that the Greeks, being so few, must be worn out with wounds and toil, returned to the attack ; but, finding as warm a welcome as the day before, they retired.

And now we have to tell of an act of treason—the blackest, perhaps, in all the annals of mankind. There was a certain Ephialtes, a Greek, native of this district, and well acquainted with the mountain paths : this man came to Xerxes, and offered to lead his army round by another way, behind the position of the Greeks at Thermopylae. Xerxes joyfully accepted the offer, and sent Hydarnes and the Immortals, with orders to take the route pointed out by Ephialtes, a steep and rugged track, leading out in the rear of the Greek position. Setting out at sundown, they toiled all night up the rocky way, and reached the summit as day was breaking. It chanced that a thousand Phocians were keeping watch over this path, which gives access to the territory of Phocis. It was a still, windless morning, and suddenly they heard the tramping of many feet crashing through the dead leaves of the oak forest which clothed the whole mountain. They ran to their arms, and at the same moment the Persians appeared. Great was the astonishment of Hydarnes, and no less his alarm, at finding himself face to face with an armed force ; for he supposed them to be Spartans. Learning from Ephialtes his mistake, he drew up his men for battle. The Phocians.

being assailed by a shower of arrows, fled to a neighbouring hill, and prepared to sell their lives dearly ; but the Persians, taking no further notice of them, continued their march, and began to descend the mountain.

The position of the Greeks at Thermopylae was now desperate. They were not without warning of the approaching peril. First the prophet Megistias, after inspecting the victims, foretold their death ; then they heard of the march of Hydarnes from deserters and their own scouts. Leonidas dismissed all his allies, excepting four hundred Thebans, whom he kept with him as hostages, and seven hundred Thespians, who refused to go. He himself determined to remain, with his three hundred Spartans ; for retreat, to a Spartan, no matter from what numbers, meant disgrace utter and irretrievable : he must conquer or die—there was no other way. And an ancient oracle had told the Spartans that either their city or their king should fall by the hand of the Persians. With him remained also the prophet Megistias.

Xerxes waited to begin the last attack until about nine in the morning, so as to give those with Hydarnes time to arrive and take the Greeks in the rear. Hitherto the Greeks had fought with caution, keeping in the narrow part of the pass, and sheltering themselves behind the wall, but now they cared not for such precautions, knowing that their doom was sealed. Forth from their line of defence sallied that little band of heroes ; on came the huge host of fighting slaves, driven on to the points of the Spartan spears by the weight of myriads pressing behind, where the officers stood urging them on with the lash. Hundreds were trampled to death, or thrust into the sea, by their own comrades. And so the carnage continued, until most of the Spartan spears were broken, and they began to use their swords. At last Leonidas fell, and over his body the battle raged afresh. Four times the

Persians were repulsed, and the Spartans rescued the body of their King. Suddenly a shout was heard in the rear, and Hydarnes and the ten thousand came pouring in through the other end of the pass. Then the Spartans knew that their last hour was come; they retired to a small hillock in the mouth of the pass, and stood waiting for death. Round them surged the yelling multitudes of cowardly foes, plying them with arrows, javelins, and stones. Still they fought on, while breath remained in their bodies; then one by one they sank down, under the storm of iron, and at last nothing was left of all that matchless band but a motionless heap.

One or two anecdotes are told in connexion with the battle which are worth repeating, as illustrating the Spartan character. A certain Greek tried to excite the fears of one of the Spartans by telling him that the clouds of Persian arrows would darken the sun. "So much the better," answered the Spartan; "we shall fight in the shade." Two other Spartans had been left in a neighbouring village, suffering from a severe complaint of the eyes. One of them, by name Eurytus, when he heard that Hydarnes was on the way to attack Leonidas in the rear, called for his arms, ordered his servant to lead him to the battlefield (for he was blind), and perished with the three hundred. The other, Aristodemus, on his return to Sparta, found himself shunned by his equals, and pointed at as a dishonoured man; he was branded with a shameful name, the most hateful to Spartan ears, that of "runaway."

Pillars were set up in the pass to commemorate this great fight. On one of them was this inscription:

> Go, traveller, to Sparta tell,
> That here, obeying her, we fell.

On the little hillock of the last resistance was placed the

figure of a stone lion, in memory of Leonidas, so fitly
named the lion-like. On it were engraved these words,
supposed to be spoken by the lion :

> A lion thou wast, in deed as well as name ;
> Therefore I watch thy tomb, and guard thy fame.

H. L. HAVELL, *Stories from Herodotus* (adapted)

THE RETREAT OF THE TEN THOUSAND

WHEN Darius,[1] the King of Persia, died, his great empire
passed to his elder son, Artaxerxes. The younger brother,
Cyrus,[2] determined to win the empire for himself, collected at Sardis a huge army, including ten thousand
Greeks. He led this host through Asia Minor, and down
the Euphrates to the very gates of Babylon itself. At
Cunaxa there was a great battle, but Cyrus was killed in
the moment of victory, so that the Greeks found themselves without a leader, and deserted by most of the
Oriental troops. At this critical time Xenophon, a young
Athenian, took the lead, and under his direction the
Greeks, harassed by the forces of the Persian King and by
hostile tribes, made a terrific march back through entirely
unknown country to the shores of the Black Sea. The
story of this adventure was told by Xenophon in a book
called the *Anabasis*, or *The March Up-country*.

They marched on through flat country and came to a
palace surrounded by many villages, full of everything
they needed. While they were encamping during the

---

[1] Three Persian kings of the name Darius are mentioned in
this book: (1) The Darius whose army was defeated at Marathon
in 490 B.C., and who was succeeded by his son Xerxes ; (2) the
Darius who was the father of Artaxerxes and Cyrus (he died in
404 B.C.) ; (3) the Darius who was dethroned by Alexander the Great
in 330 B.C.

[2] Two Persians named Cyrus are mentioned : (1) The Cyrus who
defeated Croesus in 546 B.C. ; (2) the Cyrus who was killed at
Cunaxa in 401 B.C.

M

night there was a heavy snowstorm, and at dawn the
decided to billet the regiments and their generals in th
villages ; for there was no enemy in sight, and they fe
safe because of the deep snow. There they had goo
food, fat animals, corn, excellent old wine, dried grape
and all kinds of vegetables. But some stragglers from th
camp said that at night they saw the light of a great man
watch-fires ; so the generals decided that it was safe
not to live scattered in billets, but to keep the whole arm
together as before. So they encamped all together, an
there seemed promise of fine weather ; but at nigh
there was such a heavy fall of snow that it covered up th
men as they lay asleep and their arms ; and the anima
were standing in deep snow. No one wanted to get u
for the snow which had fallen on them kept them warn
if they lay still, except where it had slipped away. The
Xenophon ventured to get up and chop wood in his tuni
and at once others followed and taking the wood fro
him began to chop too. After that others got up an
lighted fires and oiled themselves.

The next day they resolved to march on as quickly a
possible before the enemy could occupy the pass. S
they struck camp and marched away at once through dee
snow with many guides, and the same day they crosse
the pass and pitched their camp. From there they marche
three stages through the desert to the river Euphrates an
crossed it waist-deep in water. From there they marche
three stages through flat country buried in snow. Th
third stage was difficult, for a north wind blew in the
faces, drying up everything and freezing the men. Th
snow was six feet deep, so that many of the transpo
animals and slaves were lost, and about thirty of th
soldiers. They made fires all night, for there was plent
of wood where they halted, and wherever a fire wa
burning the snow melted, and great trenches were mad

ight down to the bare ground, and there they were able
o measure the depth of the snow. The next day they
marched on through the snow, and many of the men
were seized with ravenous hunger.

Parties of the enemy harassed their rear, plundering
abandoned transport animals and fighting over them with
one another. Soldiers were abandoned too who had been
struck with snow-blindness and whose frost-bitten toes
had become septic. For their eyes they found protection
from the snow by keeping something black in front of
them on the march; for their feet the only course was to
keep on the move without stopping, and to take off their
sandals at night; if they slept in their sandals the straps
worked into the flesh, and the sandals were firmly frozen
to their feet. This kind of thing drove some of the men
to fall out and sit down, refusing to march any farther.
But Xenophon, who was with the rearguard, noticed them
and begged them with all the persuasion he could use not
to get left behind, because hordes of the enemy were at
their heels; at last he got angry with them; but they
told him to cut their throats, for they could not move a
step farther.

Then Xenophon decided it was best to frighten off the
enemy behind him and so to protect the disabled. Then
he marched on, promising the sick men that some one
should come for them next day, but before he had gone
half a mile he came on soldiers lying down in the snow,
wrapped in their cloaks, without any sentries; so he made
them get up. They said that the men in front were not
moving on. So Xenophon passed them and sent forward
picked men from his light infantry to find out what was
stopping them. They reported that the whole army was
lying down in the same way. So Xenophon's men had to
bivouac there without fires or supper, putting out what
sentries they could. At daybreak Xenophon sent his

youngest men back to the sick with orders to force them
to get up and go on.

The rest marched on and after a few miles came to the
village where Cheirisophus[1] was quartered ; they decided
it was safe to billet the regiments in the different villages.
Cheirisophus stayed there, and the rest drew lots for the
villages they could see.   Here Polycrates, an Athenian
officer, asked for leave and ran off to the village which
had fallen to Xenophon's lot.   There he captured all the
villagers and the village headman and seventeen young
horses, which were being reared as tribute for the King,
and the headman's daughter, who had been married a
week ; her husband was out hunting hares, so he was not
captured in the village.   The houses were underground,
with entrances like the mouth of a well, but down below
they were roomy ;   the entrances for animals were dug
out of the earth, but men went down a ladder.   In the
house were goats, sheep, oxen, birds, and their young
ones ;   all the animals were reared underground on green
fodder.   They had wheat, barley, vegetables, and beer
in bowls.   There were reeds in it, some long, some short
without joints ;   anyone who was thirsty had to suck the
beer through one of these.

Xenophon made the headman of the village sit down to
supper with him and told him not to be afraid, for they
would not rob him of his children and would pay him
back for all their food before they left.   He was very
friendly and showed them where the wine-cellar was.
The next day Xenophon took the headman and made a
round of the villages, and everywhere found the men
having good meals and enjoying themselves ;   nowhere
would they let them go without giving them breakfast ;
everywhere they spread on one table lamb, kid, pork, veal,
fowls, with many loaves both of wheat and barley bread.

[1] One of the Greek generals ; he led the vanguard.

They offered the headman any present he liked to choose, but he would accept nothing unless he saw any of his relations, whom he always took away with him. When they came to Cheirisophus they found his men too in their billets wearing garlands of hay, and Armenian boys waiting on them in their Oriental dress. They had to make signs to the boys to show them what they wanted as though they were deaf and dumb. Then Cheirisophus and Xenophon questioned the headman through the interpreter, who spoke Persian, and asked him the name of the country ; he replied, " Armenia."

From there they marched to a big, wealthy city with a large population, called Gymnias, and the governor of the territory sent a guide to the Greeks to lead them through a district hostile to his own. When he arrived he said he would take them in five days to a place from which they would see the sea. " If I don't," he said, " you can kill me." So he led the way, and as soon as they got into the hostile territory he urged them to burn and plunder ; indeed, it was quite clear that he had come on purpose for this, and not out of any affection for the Greeks.

On the fifth day they came to a mountain which was called Theches. As soon as the first men reached the top and saw the sea there was a great shouting ; and Xenophon with the rearguard thought, when they heard it, that there was a party of the enemy in front ; for they were already being harassed in the rear after laying waste the country. But as the shouts became louder and nearer they rushed forward on one another's heels, joining in the shouting as they came up, so that the noise grew greater as more of them came on. Then Xenophon knew something extraordinary had happened, and, jumping on his horse, galloped to the rescue with Lycius and the cavalry. And soon they heard the soldiers shouting and passing on the word from one to another, " The sea ! The sea ! "

Then they all came running up, rearguard as well, the transport and cavalry galloping. When they all reached the top they began embracing one another, generals and officers as well, and weeping. And suddenly the word went round, and the soldiers brought stones and built a great cairn, and left there as offerings a lot of untanned hides and sticks and captured shields.

DORA PYM, *Readings from the Literature of Ancient Greece* (adapted)

ALEXANDER THE GREAT

[BORN in Macedonia in 356 B.C., Alexander succeeded his father at the age of twenty, and in thirteen years he had extended his rule over all the known regions of Asia and Egypt. Many stories are told of this great conqueror. The following are taken from his biography in *Lives of Famous Greeks and Romans*. These *Lives* were written by a Greek named Plutarch, who lived near Athens during the last half of the first century after Christ. It was from a translation of this book, made during his own lifetime, that Shakespeare obtained the stories for such plays as *Julius Caesar* and *Coriolanus*.]

For many kinds of glory Alexander cared little ; unlike his father Philip, who prided himself on his oratorical powers, and used to record his victories in the chariot races at Olympia upon his coins. Indeed, when Alexander's friends, to try him, asked him whether he would contend in the foot race at Olympia, for he was a remarkably swift runner, he answered, " Yes, if I have kings to contend with."

Whenever he heard of Philip's having taken some city,

or won some famous victory, he used to look unhappy at the news, and would say to his friends, " Boys, my father will forestall us in everything ; he will leave no great exploits for you and me to achieve."

When the famous Bucephalus was offered to Philip for the sum of thirteen talents the King and his friends proceeded to some level ground to try the horse's paces. They found that he was very savage and unmanageable, for he allowed no one to mount him, and paid no attention to any man's voice, but refused to allow anyone to approach him. On this Philip became angry, and bade them take the vicious, intractable brute away. Alexander, who was present, said, " What a fine horse they are ruining because they are too ignorant and cowardly to manage him." Philip at first was silent, but when Alexander repeated this remark several times, and seemed greatly distressed, he said, " Do you blame your elders, as if you knew more than they, or were better able to manage a horse ? " " This horse, at any rate," answered Alexander, " I could manage better than anyone else." " And if you cannot manage him," retorted his father, " what penalty will you pay for your forwardness ? " " I will pay," said Alexander, " the price of the horse."

While the others were laughing and settling the terms of the wager Alexander ran straight up to the horse, took him by the bridle, and turned him to the sun ; as it seems he had noticed that the horse's shadow dancing before his eyes alarmed him and made him restive. He then spoke gently to the horse, and patted him on the back with his hand, until he perceived that he no longer snorted so wildly, when, dropping his cloak, he lightly leaped upon his back. He now steadily reined him in, without violence or blows, and as he saw that the horse was no longer ill-tempered, but only eager to gallop, he let him go, boldly urging him to full speed with his voice and heel.

Philip and his friends were at first silent with terror ; but when he wheeled the horse round, and rode up to them exulting in his success, they burst into a loud shout. It is said that his father wept for joy, and, when he dismounted, kissed him, saying, " My son, seek for a kingdom worthy of yourself : for Macedonia will not hold you."

.   .   .   .   .   .

The Greeks assembled at Corinth and agreed to invade Persia with Alexander for their leader. Many of their chief statesmen and philosophers paid him visits of congratulation, and he hoped that Diogenes, who was at that time living at Corinth, would do so. As he, however, paid no attention whatever to Alexander and remained quietly at home, Alexander himself went to visit him. He found him lying at full length, basking in the sun. At the approach of so many people, he sat up, and looked at Alexander. Alexander greeted him, and inquired whether he could do anything for him. " Yes," answered Diogenes, " you can stand a little on one side and not keep the sun off me." This answer is said to have so greatly surprised Alexander, and to have filled him with such a feeling of admiration for the greatness of mind of a man who could treat him with such insolent superiority, that when he went away, while all around were jeering and scoffing, he said, " Say what you will ; if I were not Alexander I would be Diogenes."

.   .   .   .   .   .

In pursuit of Darius he rode more than five hundred miles in eleven days, so that his men were terribly distressed, especially by want of water. One day he met some Macedonians who were carrying water from a river in skins on the backs of mules. Seeing Alexander faint with thirst, as it was the hottest time of the day, they quickly filled a helmet with water and gave it to him to drink. He asked them to whom they were carrying the water, to which they answered, " To our own sons ; but provided that you live, even if they should die, we can beget other children." On hearing this he took the helmet in his hands ; but seeing all the horsemen around him eagerly watching him and coveting the water, he gave it back without tasting it. He thanked the men for offering it to him, but said, " If I alone drink it, all these soldiers will be discontented." The soldiers, when they saw the noble courage and self-denial of Alexander, bade him lead them on boldly, and urged forward their horses, saying that they felt neither hunger nor thirst, and did not think themselves to be mortal men, so long as they had such a king as Alexander to lead them.

DORA PYM, *Readings from the Literature of Ancient Greece*

[Another story tells how when he came to Gordium Alexander was shown, preserved in the temple, the ancient chariot of Gordius, the king of Phrygia and father of Midas. The yoke was fastened to the pole by a curiously twisted knot of the fibres of the cornel-tree, and an oracle had declared that whosoever should untie this knot should become lord of Asia. Try as he might, Alexander could not unloose it, so he cut it with his sword. To " cut the Gordian knot " has become proverbial for finding a short, bold way out of a difficulty.]

HORATIUS

LARS PORSENA of Clusium
   By the Nine Gods he swore
That the great house of Tarquin
   Should suffer wrong no more.
By the Nine Gods he swore it,
   And named a trysting-day,

And bade his messengers ride forth,
East and west and south and north,
     To summon his array.

    .   .   .   .

And now hath every city
     Sent up her tale of men ;
The foot are fourscore thousand,
     The horse are thousands ten.
Before the gates of Sutrium
     Is met the great array ;
A proud man was Lars Porsena
     Upon the trysting-day.

    .   .   .   .

But by the yellow Tiber
     Was tumult and affright :
From all the spacious champaign
     To Rome men took their flight.[1]

When the enemy approached every one sought safety by
going into the city from the open country ; the city itself
they strengthened with guards. Most parts of it were
protected either by walls or by the barrier of the river
Tiber ; the Sublician Bridge would have offered an open
way in for the enemy if it had not been for one man—
Horatius Cocles ; he was the bulwark that the good
fortune of the city of Rome had on that day. He happened to be posted as sentry at the bridge, when he saw the
Janiculum Hill taken with a sudden rush, and the forces
of the enemy pouring down its slopes, while a terrified
mob of his fellow-citizens abandoned their arms and
broke their ranks ; he rebuked them one after another and
tried to stop them, swearing solemnly by the faith of
gods and men, and calling them to witness that it was

[1] From Macaulay's *Lays of Ancient Rome*. The interpolation of
these lines, and of those on p. 188, is the present editor's.

useless to desert their posts and run away. "If you leave the river unguarded behind you," he cried, "there will soon be more of the enemy on the Palatine and the Capitol than there are on the Janiculum now. Destroy the bridge with tools, with fire, with anything you can ! I will hold back the enemy as long as one man's body can keep them at bay."

Then he went to the far end of the bridge and stood out above the vast crowd of fugitives, whose backs were turned to the foe ; for he faced them with his arms ready for a hand-to-hand fight ; by the miracle of his boldness he stupefied the enemy. Two men, however, driven by shame, kept beside him—Spurius Larcius and Titus Herminius, both of them of high birth and reputation. With these for a little while Horatius endured the first storm of danger and the fiercest part of the battle ; then these two also he forced to go back into safety, for only a small part of the bridge was left, and the men who were cutting it down were calling them back. Then he rolled his fierce eyes threateningly on the Tuscan princes and challenged them to single combat ; then he taunted them all, shouting, "You are slaves of proud kings, and forgetting your own liberty you come to attack the liberty of others." They hesitated for a little, while they looked from one to another waiting for some one to attack him ; at last, moved by shame, they raised a shout, and all together they hurled their spears at their single foe. He caught them all on his shield, and with the same determination kept his feet firmly planted on the bridge when they tried to bear him down by the weight of their attack.

Just then the broken bridge cracked and the Romans shouted with joy that the work was finished, and a sudden panic stayed the onrush of the enemy. Then Horatius cried, "O Father Tiber, O river-god, I pray thee, receive

a soldier and his armour with kindly wave." So, armed
as he was, he leaped down into the Tiber, and, in spite
of the shower of spears which fell about him, swam safely
across to his own people.

> And now he feels the bottom ;
>   Now on dry earth he stands ;
> Now round him throng the Fathers
>   To press his gory hands ;
> And now, with shouts and clapping,
>   And noise of weeping loud,
> He enters through the River-Gate,
>   Borne by the joyous crowd.
>
> They gave him of the corn-land,
>   That was of public right,
> As much as two strong oxen
>   Could plough from morn till night ;
> And they made a molten image,
>   And set it up on high,
> And there it stands unto this day
>   To witness if I lie.

DORA PYM, *Readings from the Literature of
Ancient Rome*

REGULUS

[THE two great cities of Rome and Carthage fought for the
supremacy of the Mediterranean in three wars generally
called the Punic Wars. It was during the first war, which
lasted from 264 B.C. to 241 B.C., that Regulus, then a
prisoner in the hands of the Carthaginians, was sent to
Rome with proposals for peace.]

Regulus was kept a close prisoner, pining and sickening
in his loneliness, while the war continued, and at last a

victory so decisive was gained by the Romans that the
people of Carthage were discouraged, and resolved to ask
terms of peace. They thought that no one would be so
readily listened to at Rome as Regulus, and they therefore
sent him there with their envoys, having first made him
swear that he would come back to his prison if there
should neither be peace nor an exchange of prisoners.
They little knew how much more a true-hearted Roman
cared for his city than for himself—for his word than for
his life.

Worn and dejected, the captive warrior came to the
outside of the gates of his own city, and there paused,
refusing to enter. " I am no longer a Roman citizen," he
said ; " I am but the barbarians' slave, and the Senate
may not give audience to strangers within the walls."

His wife Marcia ran out to greet him, with his two
sons, but he did not look up, and received their caresses
as one beneath their notice, as a mere slave, and he
continued, in spite of all entreaty, to remain outside the
city, and would not even go to the little farm he had
loved so well.

The Roman Senate, as he would not come in to them,
came out to hold their meeting in the Campagna.

The ambassadors spoke first ; then Regulus, standing
up, said, as one repeating a task, " Conscript fathers,
being a slave to the Carthaginians, I come on the part of
my masters to treat with you concerning peace, and an
exchange of prisoners." He then turned to go away with
the ambassadors, as a stranger might not be present at the
deliberations of the Senate. His old friends pressed him
to stay and give his opinion as a senator who had twice
been consul ; but he refused to degrade that dignity by
claiming it, slave as he was. But, at the command of his
Carthaginian masters, he remained, though not taking his
seat.

Then he spoke. He told the senators to persevere in the war. He said he had seen the distress of Carthage, and that a peace would be only to her advantage, not to that of Rome, and therefore he strongly advised that the war should continue. Then, as to the exchange of prisoners, the Carthaginian generals, who were in the hands of the Romans, were in full health and strength, whilst he himself was too much broken down to be fit for service again, and indeed he believed that his enemies had given him a slow poison, and that he could not live long. Thus he insisted that no exchange of prisoners should be made.

It was wonderful, even to the Romans, to hear a man thus pleading against himself, and their chief priest came forward, and declared that, as his oath had been wrested from him by force, he was not bound by it to return to his captivity. But Regulus was too noble to listen to this for a moment. " Have you resolved to dishonour me ? " he said. " I am not ignorant that death and the extremest tortures are preparing for me ; but what are these to the shame of an infamous action, or the wounds of a guilty mind ? Slave as I am to Carthage, I have still the spirit of a Roman. I have sworn to return. It is my duty to go ; let the gods take care of the rest."

The Senate decided to follow the advice of Regulus, though they bitterly regretted his sacrifice. His wife wept and entreated in vain that they would detain him ; they could merely repeat their permission to him to remain ; bu nothing could prevail with him to break his word, and he turned back to the chains and death he expected as calmly as if he had been returning to his home.

C. M. YONGE, *A Book of Golden Deeds*

HANNIBAL

[IN the Second Punic War the central figure was Hannibal, who in 218 B.C. made a daring invasion of Italy from Spain across the Pyrenees and the Alps.]

Hannibal marched from the river Durance through level country to the Alps, unmolested by the Gauls who lived in those parts. He and his army had learnt by report, exaggerated as all such reports generally are, what was in front of them; but when they saw the prospect with their own eyes their terror was renewed—lofty, snow-capped mountains almost touching the sky, strange huts perched on rocks, cattle and horses pinched by the cold, men shaggy and savage-looking, everything animate and inanimate frost-bound, and other things too dreadful to describe. As the line of men began to wind up the lower slopes mountain tribes appeared, posted on the overhanging hills; if they had ambushed the remote valleys and suddenly come out to fight, they would have caused great panic and slaughter. Hannibal called a halt, and sent Gallic scouts on ahead, and when he learnt that he could not get through at that point he pitched his camp in the largest open space he could find in that rocky and precipitous country.

Then he found out through the same Gauls, who were able to listen to the conversation of the mountaineers because their own language and customs were not very different, that the pass was only blocked in the day-time and at night the tribesmen went off to their homes. So at dawn he approached the hills as though he were going to force his way through the pass by day and in full view of them all. He spent the whole day in making feints to conceal his real intention, and fortified the first camp he had made; then, as soon as he knew that the mountaineers had left the hills and relaxed their guard, in order to deceive them he lighted more fires than were necessary for the number of men left in the camp ; he left the baggage, the cavalry, and most of the infantry behind, and, himself leading a picked detachment of men with light equipment, dashed quickly through the pass and took up a position on those very hills which the enemy had held. Then at dawn the camp was struck, and the rest of his army resumed their march.

Immediately the mountaineers gave the signal and gathered from their mountain strongholds at their usual post, but suddenly they caught sight of strange men holding the point of vantage overhead and another hostile force making its way past along the road below. When they first saw and realized these two facts they stood motionless for a little while ; then they saw that the Carthaginians were afraid in the narrow pass and that the column was thrown into confusion by its own struggles, chiefly because the horses were terrified ; so they thought that if they could increase this panic it would be enough to spread complete destruction, and, being accustomed to difficult mountain paths, they rushed down from the jagged rocks near by. Then the Carthaginians were fighting against the difficulties of the road and the enemy at the same time ; and they fought more with one another than with the enemy, because each man was trying to get into safety himself. The horses did the most harm ; terrified by the harsh shouts, which the woods and valleys made louder by their echoes, they stampeded, and if they happened to be hit or wounded they were so maddened that they spread havoc among the men and all the transport animals. On each side of the road were sheer precipices, and it was so crowded that many were pushed over the edge into the abyss, amongst them a few soldiers ; some of the laden transport animals rolled over with a tremendous crash. In spite of this horrible scene Hannibal remained quiet for a little and held back his men to prevent their increasing the confusion and panic. But after he saw that the column was broken and that there was a danger of losing the baggage, which would make the safe passage of his army useless, he dashed down from the higher ground and immediately scattered the enemy by his attack. He also increased the confusion of his own men, but only for a moment; directly the road was cleared by the flight of the mountaineers they became calmer; in a short time the whole army was led through the pass, not only unmolested, but almost in complete silence. Hannibal also captured the principal stronghold of the district and the villages clustered round it, and for three days fed the army on the booty and cattle he had gained in this way; also, because the mountaineers were terrified at first and the road was not very difficult, he was able to cover some ground in those three days.

Next they came to another of the many mountain tribes, a people mainly engaged in agriculture. Here Hannibal was almost overcome, not by open warfare, but by his own weapons, deceit and trickery. The oldest men of the mountain strongholds came as ambassadors to the Carthaginians and said, " We have learnt a wholesome lesson from the misfortunes of others, and we would rather make trial of friendship than strength with the Carthaginians; we will carry out all your orders obediently, and we ask you to accept provisions, guides for your march, and hostages to ensure our good faith."

Hannibal did not think he ought to trust them implicitly or yet to refuse their offers, for fear that if they were rejected they might become openly hostile; so he gave a gracious answer and accepted the hostages they gave and used the provisions which they themselves had brought down to the road; but he followed their guides with his column in battle array as though still in an enemy's country. The elephants and the cavalry led the way, and Hannibal himself followed with the pick of the infantry, anxious and on the alert the whole way. When they reached a narrow part of the road, which ran beneath an overhanging rock, wild tribesmen sprang up out of ambushes on all sides, in front and in rear, attacking them close at hand and from a distance, rolling down huge rocks on the column. The greatest pressure was in the rear ; the infantry turned round to face it, and certainly a great disaster would have happened in this gorge if the rear of the line had not been strengthened. As it was, the whole army came within a hairbreadth of complete destruction ; for Hannibal hesitated to allow the march to continue through the narrow defile because the infantry had no guard in the rear corresponding to their own guard in the rear of the cavalry ; the mountaineers seized the opportunity to attack from the side, and cutting the line in two occupied the road ; so Hannibal spent one night cut off from the cavalry and transport.

The next day the barbarian attacks weakened, and he was able to join forces again and get through the defile ; he had some losses, but more among animals than men. After that the tribesmen attacked in smaller numbers to plunder rather than to fight ; sometimes they attacked in front, sometimes in the rear, whenever the nature of the ground made it easy, or an advance or halt gave them an opportunity. Although it took a long time to lead elephants along these steep and narrow roads, yet wherever they were they gave protection against the enemy, who dared not go near them because they had never seen such creatures before.

On the ninth day they reached the top of the Alps by rough paths ; they had lost their way many times either through the deceit of their guides or the rashness of some

who, distrusting the guides, tried different valleys, guessing
at the right road. For two days they halted at the top,
and the soldiers were allowed to rest after their hard
work and fighting ; some transport animals which had
fallen down among the rocks followed the track of the
march and made their way into the camp. The men
were worn out and depressed at their countless hardships,
and when the constellation of the Pleiades was setting a
heavy fall of snow caused great terror. The camp was
broken up at dawn, and, as the men marched slowly
through the deep snow-drifts with depression and despair
written on all their faces, Hannibal stepped in front of
the standards and ordered the men to halt on a jutting-out
peak of rock, which commanded a very wide view ; he
showed them Italy, pointing to the plains around the
river Po, which lie at the foot of the Alps, and said : " You
are climbing the walls not of Italy alone, but of Rome
herself ; the rest will all be straightforward and easy ;
after one or two battles at most you will hold and control
in your power the very citadel and capital of Italy." Then
the line began to advance, for now even the enemy only
attempted petty thefts from time to time. The rest of
the march was more difficult than the ascent had been,
for the Italian slopes of the Alps are shorter but also
steeper. Almost the whole of the road was precipitous,
narrow, and slippery, so that they could not help falling
down ; and even if they slipped a little they could not
regain their footing, and they fell on top of one another,
the animals on their drivers.

Next they came to the narrowest pass of all, where the
rocks were so sheer that an adventurous soldier without
equipment could hardly let himself down, even by clinging
to the shrubs and trunks of trees which stood out from
the rock. Nature had made the place precipitous, and a
recent landslide had torn away the ground to the depth of

about a thousand feet. The cavalry halted as though it were the end of the road, and a message was sent back to Hannibal, who was wondering what was the cause of the halt, that the rock was impassable. So he went himself to look at the place ; it seemed quite clear that he would have to lead his column a long way round by pathless ways never trodden before. But this road was hopeless ; for on top of the old untrodden snow freshly fallen snow was lying moderately deep ; this offered a good foothold for the first men who trod on it, since it was soft and not very deep ; when it collapsed under the weight of such a crowd of men and animals they were marching over bare ice through the liquid mud of melting snow. There was a terrible struggle, for the slippery ice gave no foothold and quickly tripped men up on the slope, and even if they helped themselves up by their hands and knees these props themselves slipped, and they fell down again with them ; there were no tree-trunks or roots round about to which a man could cling with foot or hand, and so they floundered about on the smooth ice and in the melting snow. Animals here and there trod a way through to the bottom layer of snow as they walked on it, and if they fell they kicked more fiercely in their struggles and so broke further into it ; many of them stuck in the hard, deeply frozen ice as though they were caught in a trap.

At length, when men and beasts had been exhausted to no purpose, a camp was pitched on the ridge ; it was very difficult to clear a space for it because so much snow had to be dug out and carted away. Then soldiers were detailed to make a road over the rock by which alone they could continue their march. They had to split the rock open and so threw down huge trunks of trees all round it, and lopping off the branches made a great pile of firewood ; this they kindled as soon as a strong enough wind had arisen to fan the fire, and when the rocks were molten they poured in vinegar so that they crumbled. Then while the rock was hot from the fire they flattened it with tools and relieved the steepness of the sides by making gentler slopes, so that even elephants could be led down as well as ordinary transport animals. They spent four days near the rock, and the animals almost died of hunger ; for the mountain peaks were practically bare, and the snow covered any fodder there was ; the lower slopes had some valleys and sunny hills and streams bordered by woods and country more fit for men to live in ; there they sent the animals to graze, and the men, tired out by making the road, were allowed three days for rest. Then they went down into the plains, where there was pleasanter country and the people were not so savage.

DORA PYM, *Readings from the Literature of Ancient Rome*

THE ERUPTION OF VESUVIUS

IN A.D. 79 Vesuvius burst into eruption. The shores of the Bay of Naples were lined, as they are to-day, with the seaside homes of the wealthy. Three popular resorts, Pompeii, Herculaneum, and Stabiae, quite close to the foot of the volcano, were completely buried in ashes. At this time Pliny was staying with his mother at Misenum, near the north end of the bay, in the villa of his uncle, who held a high command in the Roman fleet. Tacitus, the historian, wishing to secure for his history an eyewitness's account of the eruption, wrote to his friend Pliny, and the following letters contain the descriptions which he received :

MY DEAR TACITUS,

You ask me to write you an account of my uncle's death, in order that you may hand it down accurately to posterity. I am grateful to you, for I see that his death, if celebrated by your pen, will attain undying fame. For, though he perished along with whole peoples and cities in a disaster which overwhelmed one of the fairest spots on our coast, in a disaster so remarkable as to secure that at least he will not be forgotten, though, besides this, he had written many books that will be remembered, yet the undying fame of your writings will help to keep his memory green. So I am ready, nay anxious, to do what you ask.

My uncle was at Misenum in supreme command of the fleet. On August 24th, about one o'clock in the afternoon, my mother drew his attention to the appearance of a cloud, unusually large and of a strange shape. He had taken a sun-bath followed by a cold bath, and was lying down after lunch, reading. He immediately put on his shoes and climbed to a spot whence he could better see this phenomenon. None of the people who were looking at the cloud from a distance were certain from which mountain it was coming (we found out afterward that it was Vesuvius) ; it was more like a pine-tree than anything else, for it shot up into a trunk of great height and then spread out into several branches. Sometimes it looked white, sometimes spotted, as though it had drawn up earth or cinders.

To a scholar like my uncle a natural phenomenon of this magnitude seemed worthy of closer study. So he ordered a launch and said I could go with him if I liked. But I said that I would rather go on with my studies, for, as it happened, he had given me some writing to do. Just as he was leaving the house a note came from Rectina, the wife of Bassus, who was terrified at the approaching danger ; his villa stood just below ours, and there was no means of escape except by sea ; she begged my uncle to save her from this perilous position. So he changed his mind and went out in the guise of a rescuer rather than a scientific observer. Large boats were launched, and he embarked with the intention of carrying help not only to Rectina, but to many others who lived along that shore because it was so picturesque. Therefore he hastened in the direction whence fugitives were coming, and steered a straight course for the point of danger ; so free from fear was he that he dictated and noted down all the motions and shapes of that terrible portent as he went along.

Already ashes were falling on the ships, and the nearer they drew the hotter and thicker grew the showers ; then came pumice-stones and other stones, blackened and scorched and cracked by fire, while the sea ebbed suddenly and the shore was blocked by landslides. The steersman was for turning back, and my uncle hesitated for a moment, and then said to him, " Fortune favours the brave. Try to reach Pomponianus." Pomponianus was at Stabiae, right across the corner of the bay (for the sea sweeps far into the curving shore just there), where the danger was not yet close at hand ; but it was in full view and certain to come nearer as it spread, so he had packed up and gone into a boat, ready to push off directly the contrary wind fell. This wind blew my uncle into Stabiae, and he embraced Pomponianus, who was trembling with fright, cheering him up and encouraging him ; in order to calm his friend's fears by showing how safe he felt himself, he ordered a bath, after which he sat down to dinner in high good humour, or at least he managed to assume a mask of good humour, which is equally wonderful.

Meanwhile, broad sheets of flame broke out all over Mount Vesuvius, rising high in the air and lighting up the sky, their brightness silhouetted against the darkness of the night. My uncle tried to quiet people's fears by saying that fires had been left burning by terrified peasants when they deserted their houses, which were now in flames and causing this light. Then he went to bed and really slept, for, being a stout man, he breathed heavily and loudly, so that he was heard by the people who were waiting about outside his door. But the courtyard which led to his room was covered to such a depth under a drift of ashes and pumice-stones that if he had stayed in bed any longer he would not have been able to get out of the door.

So he was wakened and joined Pomponianus and the others, who had been keeping watch. They consulted together as to whether it would be better to stay under cover or to go wandering about in the open. For the house was beginning to totter under the frequent and violent earthquakes, and it seemed to rock to and fro as though it had been shaken from its foundations. On the other hand, if they went outside they had the falling pumice-stones to fear, though, being porous, they were light. After comparing the two risks they chose the latter. They tied pillows on their heads with table-cloths; this was their only protection against the showers of stones and ashes.

Day had now dawned elsewhere, but with them was darkness, blacker and deeper than the deepest night, though here and there it was relieved by torches and other lights. They decided to go down to the shore in order to see from close at hand whether the sea would allow them to get away, but the waves were still high and contrary. There my uncle lay down on a disused sail, and again and again called for cold water, which he drank. Then flames, heralded by a strong smell of sulphur, put the others to flight and roused him. Leaning on two slaves he managed to stand up, but instantly fell down again; I think his breathing was blocked by the thick fumes, which choked the narrow passage of his throat; it was never very strong and often got inflamed. When daylight returned—three days after his death—his body was found without any wound or scar, covered with the clothes he had been wearing. He looked more like a man asleep than dead.

Meantime, Mother and I were at Misenum. But you don't want to hear about anything but my uncle's death, so I will close. Let me add that I have related either what I witnessed myself or heard at the time, when one gets the truest accounts. You will pick out what you want. For it is one thing to write a letter to a friend, and quite another to write a history for the general public.

Good-bye.

PLINY

MY DEAR TACITUS,

You say that the letter I wrote you at your request, describing my uncle's death, has made you anxious to know what terrors and dangers I endured, left behind at Misenum.

After my uncle had gone I spent the rest of the day in study; for I had stayed at home for this purpose. Then I had a bath and supper and went to bed, but I got little sleep and that only in snatches. For several days beforehand we had had earthquakes, which did not alarm us much, as they are common in Campania. But that night the shocks were so violent that the very universe seemed to be uprooted. Mother rushed into my bedroom; I was just getting up, meaning to wake her if she was asleep. We sat down in the courtyard of the house, which separated us by a small space from the sea. I don't know whether I ought to be called brave or foolhardy—I was only seventeen—but I sent for a volume of Livy, the historian, and went on reading it and even copying extracts from it, as though to-morrow would not do.

Then in came a friend of my uncle's, who had lately arrived from Spain to visit him; seeing Mother and me sitting there and me actually reading, he spoke sharply to me for being so confident and to her for putting up with it. But I took no notice and remained glued to my book.

It was now six o'clock in the morning, but the light was still faint and tired-looking. The buildings round us were already trembling, and, though we stood on open ground, we should certainly be in danger if they fell. Then we decided to leave the town. When we got beyond the houses we stopped, and there went through an experience which was wonderful but very terrible. The carriages we had ordered to come with us could not keep still, even though they were on level ground and wedged with stones ; we saw the sea sucked back to its inmost depths, and driven back by the shaking of the earth. On the other side a black, dreadful cloud of fiery vapour yawned open, bursting into weird ribbons of fire, with twisting, forked tongues of flame ; they were like flashes of lightning, only larger.

Then the Spanish friend took command, and said sharply : "If your brother—your uncle [turning to me]— is still alive, he wants you to be saved ; if he is dead he wants you to survive him. Why do you hesitate and linger here ? " We said that our own safety was nothing to us if we were uncertain of his. So our friend waited no longer, but rushed away from the danger-zone, as fast as he could go.

Soon afterward the cloud came down upon the earth and covered the sea ; it had encircled and hidden the island of Capri and even blotted out Cape Misenum. Then Mother began to beg and pray and finally to order me to escape as best as I could. " You are young," she said, " I am old and good for nothing. I shall die happy if only I have not caused your death." I said that I would not be saved without her, so I took her by the hand and made her hurry along. Already ashes were falling, but only here and there ; I looked behind me, and saw dense blackness just at our backs, spreading over the earth like a torrent. "Let us turn aside," I said, "while we can see; then we shan't be knocked down in the road and trampled on by the crowds in the dark."

We had hardly sat down before blackness overtook us, not the blackness of a cloudy or moonless night, but of a room that is shut up with the lamp out. You could hear women shrieking, children screaming, men shouting; some were looking for their parents, others for their children, and others for their wives or husbands, able to recognize them only by their voices; one man would be lamenting his own fate; another the fate of his dear ones; some in terror of death were praying to die. Many were praying to the gods; but most declared that the gods were no more, and that this was the last eternal night of the world.

Gradually it grew light; we did not think it was daylight, but only the sign of approaching fire; however, the fire did not come very near us, and the darkness fell again, and another heavy shower of ashes. All the time we kept on getting up and shaking ourselves; otherwise we should have been buried and crushed under their weight.

At last this darkness melted away into a kind of smoke or cloud and vanished; then followed real daylight, and even the sun came out, though it looked pale as in an eclipse. To our trembling eyes everything appeared different, being covered with deep drifts of ashes. We went back to Misenum, took what rest we could, and passed an anxious night hovering between hope and fear; fear got the upper hand, for the earthquakes were still going on. But even then, after all the dangers we had gone through with the prospect of still worse things ahead of us, we had no idea of leaving the town without news of my uncle. Please excuse all these details.

PLINY

DORA PYM, *Readings from the Literature of Ancient Rome*

HEROES

THE winds that once the *Argo* bore
    Have died by Neptune's ruined shrines,
And her hull is the drift of the deep sea-floor,
    Though shaped of Pelion's tallest pines.
You may seek her crew on every isle
    Fair in the foam of Aegean seas,
But, out of their rest, no charm can wile
    Jason and Orpheus and Hercules.

And Priam's wail is heard no more
    By windy Ilion's sea-built walls ;
Nor great Achilles, stained with gore,
    Shouts, " O ye Gods ! 'tis Hector falls ! "
On Ida's mount is the shining snow,
    But Jove has gone from its brow away ;
And red on the plain the poppies grow
    Where the Greek and the Trojan fought that day.

Mother Earth ! Are the heroes dead ?
    Do they thrill the soul of the years no more ?
Are the gleaming snows and the poppies red
    All that is left of the brave of yore ?
Are there none to fight as Theseus fought
    Far in the young world's misty dawn ?
Or to teach as the grey-haired Nestor taught ?
    Mother Earth ! are the heroes gone ?

Gone ? In a grander form they rise ;
    Dead ? We may clasp their hands in ours ;
And catch the light of their clearer eyes,
    And wreathe their brows with immortal flowers.
Wherever a noble deed is done
    'Tis the pulse of a hero's heart is stirred ;
Wherever Right has a triumph won
    There are the heroes' voices heard.

E. D. PROCTOR

LIST OF BOOKS FOR FURTHER READING

CHURCH, A. J. *The Story of the Iliad* (Seeley, Service). *The Story of the Odyssey* (Seeley, Service). *The Children's Iliad* (Seeley, Service). *The Children's Odyssey* (Seeley, Service). *The Children's Aeneid* (Seeley, Service). *Stories from Livy* (Seeley, Service). *Stories from Virgil* (Seeley, Service).

COX, SIR G. W. *Tales of the Gods and Heroes* (Nelson).

FARRAR, F. A. *Old Greek Nature Stories* (Harrap).

HAVELL, H. L. *Stories from the Iliad* (Harrap). *Stories from the Odyssey* (Harrap). *Stories from the Aeneid* (Harrap). *Stories from Greek Tragedy* (Harrap). *Stories from Herodotus* (Harrap). *Stories from Xenophon* (Harrap).

HAWTHORNE, NATHANIEL. *Tanglewood Tales. A Wonder-book.*

HYDE, L. S. *Favourite Greek Myths* (Harrap).

KINGSLEY, CHARLES. *The Heroes.*

KUPFER, GRACE H. *Legends of Greece and Rome* (Harrap).

LAMB, CHARLES. *The Adventures of Ulysses.*

LANG, ANDREW. *Tales of Troy and Greece* (Longmans).

MACAULAY, LORD. *Lays of Ancient Rome.*

MORRIS, WILLIAM. *The Life and Death of Jason* (Longmans).

STAWELL, MAYOR, AND MARVIN. *The Story of the Iliad. The Story of the Odyssey.*

STURGEON, MARY C. *Women of the Classics* (Harrap).

YONGE, CHARLOTTE M. *A Book of Golden Deeds.*

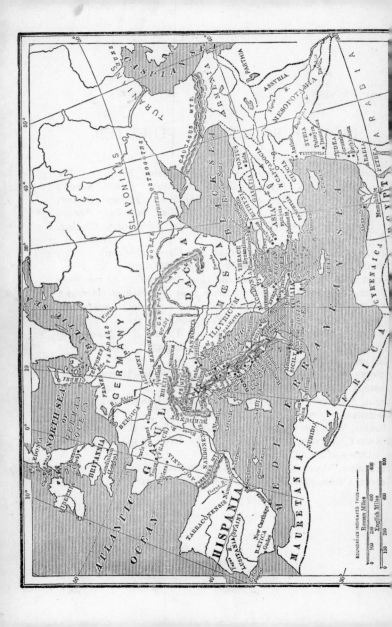

EXERCISES

THIS list of exercises is not intended to be exhaustive. It does not, for example, contain such a question as " Tell the story of Orpheus and Eurydice in your own words." Teachers, it is suggested, should see that the substance of each story is known, testing this either orally or in writing. Nor is it intended that each pupil should attempt all the questions. If the class be divided into groups, different questions may be set to different groups, and one answer read from each group and commented on by the whole class. Some of the questions may best be answered by way of a class debate ; before others are attempted the teacher may have to give guidance or supply information.

LEGENDS AND MYTHS

1. What great gift did Orpheus possess ? In a famous English poem a musician had the power to charm by his music (a) animals and (b) children, and to make them follow him. Who was he ? Tell his story as if you were one of the older inhabitants of the town or one of the children.

2. What do you consider the most exciting part of the story of Orpheus and Eurydice ?

3. Describe the journey of Orpheus down to the Underworld.

4. Trace on the map, as far as you can, the voyage of the Argonauts. Suggest how they might have reached Circe's Isle on their return journey.

5. Sketch a pen-portrait of one of the Argonauts, and then compare him with a medieval knight ready for a tournament or a modern soldier ready for battle.

6. Describe the launch of *Argo*.

7. On the return voyage the Argonauts had many adventures. Which, in your opinion, was the most exciting ?

8. Many of the paragraphs in the story of the Argonauts are written in what is sometimes called poetic prose, *e.g.*, Orpheus' song at the launch of *Argo*, the paragraph on p. 36 describing the effect of the Sirens' song, and Medeia's song to Talus. Try to put one of these into verse.

207

9. The description of the Isle of the Sirens is a good word-picture. Why is this? What devices does Kingsley use? Find other good pictures.

10. The story of the Argonauts as given in this book has been taken from three writers. Who are they? How do their stories differ in form and style?

11. Venus was the goddess of love and Diana the goddess of the chase. Of what was Demeter the goddess? What other name had she? What English word does this name give us?

12. Most of the Greek myths had a meaning. What would you suggest the story of Persephone might symbolize?

13. A poet has written:

Then unseen Perseus stole anigh the maid.

Explain why Perseus was not at first seen by Andromeda.

14. Who was Talus? In what way did he die?

15. Describe the race-course where Milanion and Atalanta ran.

16. Tell the story of the race between Milanion and Atalanta as one of the onlookers might have told it, making your story as exciting as possible.

17. Milanion's watch in the temple of Venus reminds us of the vigil kept by a medieval knight over his armour before he was knighted. Describe the scene of such a vigil.

18. "The journey from Troezene to Athens was not a long one, but it was beset by many difficulties." Use that sentence as a beginning to describe the journey of Theseus.

19. How did Ariadne show herself more resourceful than Theseus?

20. Explain the origin and meaning of these words: tantalize, ambrosial, Stygian, Herculean, Procrustean.

21. Explain the appropriateness of the epithets in these cases: that *simple* Talus; Heracles *the mighty*; the *witch-maiden* Medeia; the *dark* passages of Hades; *silver-footed* Thetis; *swift-footed* Atalanta; the *magic* bough; Sinis *the pine-bender*.

22. Say who were the following:

    (i) The prince of minstrels.
    (ii) The ferryman of Hades.
    (iii) The three-headed dog.
    (iv) Peleus' silver-footed bride.
    (v) The bride of darkness.
    (vi) The famous craftsman.
    (vii) The club-bearer.

THE STORY OF TROY

1. What was the "Apple of Discord"? How do we use the expression nowadays?

2. "Noble was the quarry, but the hunter was nobler far." Which, in your opinion, was the nobler, Hector or Achilles? With which do you sympathize in the combat? Say why.

3. Describe the manner in which the women of Troy did their washing, and compare it with the way in which it is done in this country nowadays.

4. Imagine you were one of the Greek heroes left in the Wooden Horse. Give an account of your experience and feelings.

5. Describe the armour and weapons used by the warriors at the siege of Troy.

6. In *The Fall of Troy* the past tense is sometimes suddenly changed to the present tense. What is the effect of this? What name does this tense sometimes get? Choose some well-known historical event and write two paragraphs about it. In the first give the name of the event and the time and place. In the second describe it as if you were an eyewitness.

7. "All the warning oracles which had spoken at the birth of Paris were forgotten." What were the oracles? Which was the most famous? Why did it always tell the truth? (See p. 160).

8. "Let the war be decided by the issue of this combat." Do you know of any other quarrels which were to be decided by single combat? One is mentioned in the Bible, and another in a famous English poem.

9. The Immortals of Olympus took part in the struggle at Troy, some on one side, and some on the other. Give two instances where the interference of an Immortal decided the issue.

10. Hector's dying prophecy was fulfilled when Paris mortally wounded Achilles in the heel. Find out and then tell in your own words how Achilles came to be invulnerable except in one place.

11. Sinon says that the Wooden Horse was of gigantic size to prevent it from being carried into Troy. This explanation of the size of the horse, of course, like the rest of Sinon's story, is not true. What do you think were the reasons for its great size?

o

12. Describe in your own words how these ancients buried their princes.

✓ 13. Make a list of the heroes who fought on the side of (a) the Greeks and (b) the Trojans.

14. Tell in your own words the story of the death of Paris.

15. Describe how the Greeks and Trojans chose by lot.

16. What is the figure of speech which is used frequently in the story of Troy ? Choose three of what you consider the best and explain them in your own words.

17. Explain the meaning of these expressions : (a) to fight or work like a Trojan ; (b) a hectoring person ; (c) a Cassandra-like prophecy.

18. Say who were the following :

    (i) The goddess of strife.
    (ii) The goddess of love.
    (iii) The priestess of Apollo.
    (iv) The shepherd-prince.
    (v) Commander-in-chief of the Greeks.
    (vi) Troy's chief defender.
    (vii) The fairest woman in the world.

19. Say who the following were and tell the part each played in the story of Troy : (i) Tyndareus ; (ii) Cassandra ; (iii) Thetis ; (iv) Aeneas ; (v) Sinon ; (vi) Menelaus ; (vii) Hephaistos.

THE WANDERINGS OF ODYSSEUS

1. Of the two descriptions of the land of the Lotus-eaters, which gives the more suggestive picture ? Tell why you think so.

2. Compare the form and style of the two poems on the Lotus-eaters.

3. Tell, in your own words, the effect on those who ate of the fruit of the lotus.

4 Tennyson often makes the sound echo the meaning. Find examples of this in the poem. Note particularly how he produces the slumbrous effect.

5. Describe the home of Polyphemus.

6. Give an account of the appearance, occupations, habits, and customs of the Cyclopes.

7. How did Odysseus hear the song of the Sirens and yet

escape ? Compare his passing of the Sirens with that of the Argonauts.

8. Write a prose description of the home of Calypso.

9. By what device did Penelope endeavour to delay giving an answer to the suitors ? How was her secret discovered ? Why is her device called a ruse worthy of Odysseus himself ?

10. How did Odysseus prove that he was courageous and crafty in his dealings with the suitors ?

11. How were (a) sheep, (b) swine, (c) kine connected with the wanderings of Odysseus ?

12. Both Apollo and Poseidon delayed the return of Odysseus. Why and how did they delay him ?

13. Which of the Immortals of Olympus helped Odysseus ? Where and how was the help given ?

14. Odysseus is sometimes described as the man of many wiles. Do you think the description justified ? Mention some of his wiles, and explain one of them more fully.

15. Say who were the following :

    (i) The messenger of Zeus.
    (ii) The Lotophagi.
    (iii) The son of Poseidon.
    (iv) The king of the winds.
    (v) The daughter of the Sun.

GREEK TRAGEDY

1. Describe in your own words a Greek theatre. Why would such a theatre not be suitable for our country ? What modern enclosures have we which seem like it ?

2. What was the Greek belief about the unburied dead ? What was the name of the dark stream of the Underworld ? How did ' shades ' cross it ?

3. On what two occasions did Antigone show devotion to her family ?

4. What is a *golden* deed ? Say why Antigone deserves to have her story told in a book of such deeds.

5. What did Clytemnestra do which has rendered her name infamous ? Had she any kind of justification ? Remember what happened to her daughter.

6. Pylades is called the " devoted comrade." What in the story shows that he deserved this description ?

7. What was the most barbarous of the practices of the Tauri ? How did this contrast with the usual reception given by the Greeks to strangers ?

8. What was the purpose of the sacrifice of Iphigeneia ? What other story in the book tells of a somewhat similar sacrifice ?

9. Dramatize the scene between Orestes, Pylades, and Iphigeneia when they are planning their escape. Bring out in the dialogue the various plans which they discuss.

10. Tell the story of the escape as if you were the messenger who brought the news to Thoas.

11. Say who were the following :

    (i) The great Athenian poet.
    (ii) The blind old king of Thebes.
    (iii) The timid sister.
    (iv) The priest and prophet of the Grecian host.

THE ADVENTURES OF AENEAS

1. What explanation did the ancients give of the volcano Mount Aetna ?

2. Imagine you are the rescued Greek and tell the story of what happened to you between the departure of Ulysses and the arrival of Aeneas.

3. What was the name of the river near which Evander was sacrificing to Hercules ? Tell how you know.

4. The " fetching of the cattle of Geryon " was one of the twelve labours of Hercules. Find out about it and tell the story of it in your own words. One of the other labours is mentioned in the story of Cacus. What is it ?

5. What other hero besides Aeneas had armour made by Vulcan ? Why did this hero need new armour ?

6. What kind of scenes did Vulcan show on the shield of Aeneas ? What famous sea-fight was shown ? Who were the contestants in this fight ?
    Virgil lived at the time of Augustus. Does this explain the fullness with which the fight is described ?

7. What other maiden mentioned in the stories in this book had an upbringing similar to Camilla's ? What is the woodman's lore ? Why were they both skilled in this ? In what other ways were they both skilled ?

8. Say who were the following :

    (i) The divine smith.

   (ii) The founder of Carthage.
  (iii) The father of great Rome.
  (iv) The enormous brood of Earth.
   (v) The warrior maiden.
  (vi) The virgin goddess.

FROM THE HISTORIANS

1. Who was Bacchus ?   What gift did he give to Midas ?   How did Midas discover that he had made a foolish choice ?

2. Solon gave the Athenians wise laws.   What action of his after that showed his wisdom ?

3. Tell the story of Cleobis and Biton as if you were their mother relating it to some of her friends.

4. Which was the most famous of the ancient oracles ?   Why was this oracle said to be of the two-edged kind ?   Refer to the answer given to Croesus for illustration.

5. What, and where, was Parnassus ?   What stood thereon ? Parnassus was also the haunt of the Muses.   Who were the Muses ?   What kind of book would you expect one called *An English Parnassus* to be ?

6. How did Cyrus make the cavalry of Croesus useless in battle ?

7. Two instances are given in the stories in this section of successful generals who fell in the hour of victory.   Who were they ?   Do you know of any instances from British history of men who fell in the hour of victory ?

8. At the World Olympic Games there is included a race called the Marathon.   What feat is commemorated in this ? Find out the distance from Marathon to Athens, and then tell whether a Marathon is a short race or a long one.

9. Describe in your own words the two bridges built over the Hellespont at the order of Xerxes.

10. From the information given sketch the character of Xerxes.

11. " Two such dinners and there would be nothing left for us to eat."   What was the occasion on which this remark was made ?   What is the point of the witticism ?

12. " Happily for Athens, happily for mankind, the words of Miltiades prevailed."   Explain why the vote given by Callimachus for battle was a happy one (*a*) for Athens and (*b*) for mankind.

13. From the information given in the various stories sketch the Spartan upbringing and character.

14. "The Retreat of the Ten Thousand." What other famous retreats in history do you know of?

15. Are there any incidents in the story of the retreat which prove that Xenophon was a born leader of men?

16. Imagine you were one of the Greeks in the army of Xenophon. Describe your feelings when you reached the top of Theches and saw the sea.

17. What traits of character do you think the various stories told about Alexander in this book reveal?

18. What were the events which led up to the attack of Lars Porsena on Rome? In what ways did Horatius show himself a typical Roman? How did the Romans reward him?

19. Regulus also was a typical Roman. Explain in your own words how he showed that he was.

20. "Here Hannibal was almost overcome, not by open warfare, but by his own weapons, deceit and trickery." How does this statement show you that the historian, Livy, from whose writings the story of the crossing of the Alps is taken, was a Roman and not a Carthaginian?

21. "Hannibal's invasion of Italy was so daring that it is almost incredible." Give as many reasons as you can in support of this remark.

22. What is the meaning of the phrase "a natural phenomenon"? What was the natural phenomenon which first attracted the attention of Pliny?

23. "He : : : went out in the guise of a rescuer rather than a scientific observer." Explain the meaning of this sentence from Pliny's letter.

24. How old was Pliny the Younger at the time of the eruption? What did he do that makes him doubt whether he should be called brave or foolhardy? What is your opinion of his action?

GENERAL EXERCISES

1. You will have observed that most of the gods and goddesses have two names, e.g., Demeter and Ceres, Hephaistos and Vulcan. Why is this? Write down the two names of as many as you can remember.

2. What strange beliefs must the ancients have held? Give as many examples from these stories as you can.

3.   Romans in Rome's quarrel
      Spared neither land nor gold,
      Nor son nor wife, nor limb nor life,
      In the brave days of old.

Illustrate the truth of this from these stories.

4. Two of the means used by writers to secure vividness in their narratives are (a) the ' historic present tense ' and (b) accumulation of detail. Find examples of each of these.

5. If it had been possible for you to share in *one* of the adventures described in these stories which one would you have chosen ? Give reasons for your choice.

6. From your study of these stories tell what you think were the qualities which the ancient Greeks and Romans most admired in a man.

7. One of the books from which extracts have been taken is called *Women of the Classics*. Write down the names of as many of the women mentioned in these stories as you can remember with a sentence or two about each.

8. Which of the persons mentioned in the stories does each of the following epithets most aptly describe : (a) cunning ; (b) wise ; (c) lion-like ; (d) patient ; (e) wealthy ; (f) beautiful ?

9. Which of the many persons mentioned in this volume do you most admire ? Which do you consider least worthy of admiration ? In each case give your reasons.

10. What were : (i) the Sirens ; (ii) Scylla ; (iii) Lethe ; (iv) Delphi ; (v) Parnassus ; (vi) Bucephalus ; (vii) the *Iliad* ; (viii) the *Odyssey* ; (ix) the *Aeneid* ; (x) the *Anabasis* ?

11. Who were (i) Homer ; (ii) Herodotus ; (iii) Xenophon ; (iv) Plutarch ; (v) Livy ; (vi) Virgil ?

12. Explain how these stories help you to understand the following words and phrases : titanic, Herculean, Stygian, tantalize, oracular, cereal, " Orpheus Choir," Spartan fare, Gordian knot, between Scylla and Charybdis, an odyssey, hector, work like a Trojan, a Marathon race.

13. Explain as many of the following allusions as you can :

      (i)   . . . gathering flowers,
            *Herself a fairer flower, by gloomy Dis
            Was gathered.*

      (ii)   In such a night
            Stood *Dido* with a willow in her hand
            Upon the wild sea-banks, and waft *her love*
            To come again to *Carthage*.

(iii)   I, as *Aeneas, our great ancestor,*
Did from the flames of Troy upon his shoulders
The *old Anchises bear*, so from the waves of Tiber
Did I the tired Cæsar.

(iv)   The face that launched a thousand ships,
And burnt the topless towers of Ilium.

(v)   Or bid the soul of *Orpheus* sing
Such notes as, warbled to the string,
Drew iron tears down Pluto's cheek,
And made *Hell grant what love did seek* !

(vi)   And of itself the water flies
All taste of living wight, *as once it fled*
The lip of Tantalus.

(vii)   The wrath
Of *stern Achilles* on his *foe* pursued
Thrice fugitive about Troy wall.

(viii) Every beast [was] more duteous at her call
Than *at Circean call the herd disguised.*

(ix)   Xerxes, the liberty of Greece to yoke,
Came to the sea, and over Hellespont
Bridging his way, Europe with Asia joined,
And scourged with many a stroke th' indignant waves.

(x)   That *starr'd Ethiop queen* that strove
To set her beauty's praise above
The sea-nymphs, and their power offended.

(xi)   The sad *Nine*, in Greece's evil hour,
Left *their Parnassus.*

(xii)   Of the *three hundred* grant but three
To make a new *Thermopylae* !

(xiii) Thy years are ripe, and over-ripe, *the son*
Of *Macedonian Philip* had ere these
Won Asia.

(xiv)   *Thou that singest*
Ilion's lofty temples robed in fire,
Ilion falling, Rome arising,
Wars, and filial faith, and Dido's pyre.

(xv)   Thus when I shun *Scylla*, your father, I fall into
Charybdis, your mother.

PRONOUNCING INDEX OF NAMES

A dash (‐) above the vowel denotes the long sound, as in māte, mēte, mīte, mōte, mūte, mōot.

Vowels which are not marked are short, as in rack, reck, rick, rock, ruck, rook.

The mark ′ shows the stressed syllable.

217

Calymne, Ka-lim'-ne
Calypso, Ka-lip'-so
Camilla, Kam-il'-a
Cassandra, Kas-san'-dra
Cassiopoeia, Kas-si-o-pē'-ya
Castor, Kas'-tor
Cepheus, Sē'-fūs
Cerberus, Ser'-ber-us
Ceres, Sē'-rēz
Chalciope, Kal-sī'-o-pe
Charon, Kā'-ron
Charybdis, Ka-rib'-dis
Cheirisophus, Kī-ri'-so-fus
Cheiron, Kī'-ron
Cicon, Ki'-kon
Circe, Sir'-se
Cleobis, Klē'-o-bis
Cleopatra, Klē-o-pat'-ra
Clusium, Klū'-si-um
Clytemnestra, Kli-tem-nes'-tra
Cocles, Kō'-klēz
Colchian, Kol'-ki-an
Colchis, Kol'-kis
Colonus, Ko-lōn'-us
Coriolanus, Kor-i-o-lā'-nus
Corynetes, Kor-i-nē'-tēz
Creon, Krē'-on
Creusa, Kre-ū'-sa
Croesus, Krē'-sus
Crommyon, Krom'-mi-on
Ctesippus, Tēs-ip'-pus
Cunaxa, Kū-nak'-sa
Cutaia, Kū-tī'-a
Cybele, Sib'-e-le
Cyclopes, Sī-klō'-pēz
Cyclops, Sī'-klops
Cyrus, Sī'-rus
Cytherea, Sith-er-ē-a
Cyzicus, Si'-zik-us

Daedalus, Dē'-da-lus
Dardanus, Dar'-da-nus
Darius, Da-rī'-us
Deiphobus, De-if'-o-bus
Delos, Dē'-los
Demaratus, Dē-mar-ā'-tus
Demeter, Dē-mē'-ter
    (or Dē-mē-ter)

Diana, Dī-an'-a
Dido, Dī'-do
Diogenes, Dī-oj'-e-nēz
Diomede, Dī'-o-mēd
Dis, Dis
Dodona, Dō-dō'-na

Eleusis, El-ū'-sis
Elysian, E-liz'-i-an
Enceladus, En-sel'-a-dus
Ephialtes, Ef-i-al'-tēz
Eretria, Er-et'-ri-a
Erginus, Er-jī'-nus
Eris, Er'-is
Eteocles, E-tē'-o-klēz
Euboea, Ū-bē'-a
Eumaeus, Ū-mē'-us
Eumenides, Ū-men'-i-dēz
Eurotas, Ū-ro'-tas
Eurycleia, Ū-ri-klī'-a
Eurydice, Ū-rid'-i-se
Eurylochus, Ū-ril'-o-kus
Eurymachus, Ū-ri'-ma-kus
Eurytus, Ū'-ri-tus
Euxine, Ux'-in
Evander, E-van'-der

Geryon, Ge'-ri-on
Gordium, Gor'-di-um
Gorgon, Gor'-gon
Gymnias, Gim'-ni-as

Hades, Hā'-dēz
Haliacmon, Hal-i-ak'-mon
Halys, Ha'-lis
Hector, Hek'-tor
Hecuba, Hek'-ū-ba
Helios, Hē'-li-os
Hellas, Hel'-las
Helle, Hel'-le (or Hel'-lē)
Hellespont, Hel'-les-pont
Hephaistos, Hē-fīs'-tos
Hera, Hē'-ra
Heracles, Hē'-ra-klēz
Herculaneum, Her-kū-lā'-ne-um
Herculean, Her-kū'-li-an
Hercules, Her'-kū-lēz
Hermes, Her'-mēz
Herminius, Her-min'-i-us